THE
LOTTERY WINNER'S
GREATEST RIDE

. . . . .

A MILLIONAIRE, A YOUNG REPORTER...
AND A JOURNEY TO FIND WHAT MATTERS MOST

SKIP JOHNSON

"All God's angels come to us disguised."

—James Russell Lowell

Cover and interior design by Dino Marino

Copy editing by Jessica Andersen

Proofreading by Linda Dutro

Paperback ISBN: 978-1-7352511-9-6

eBook ISBN: 979-8-9871654-0-9

Other Books by Skip Johnson

The Mystic's Gift:
A Story About Loss, Letting Go . . .
and Learning to Soar

(Book 1 in The Mystic's Gift/ Royce Holloway series)

A spellbinding, deeply moving story that is quickly becoming a self-help classic. Following a sudden, unimaginable personal tragedy at a point in his midlife where Royce Holloway thought he had it all, he is introduced to a wise, exotic, enchanting mentor named Maya, who takes Royce on a powerful journey of courageous self-discovery and incredible possibilities.

What he learns on this captivating, often poignant trek across two continents will change him in a powerful way, but you may find that the life changed most . . . is yours.

The Gentleman's Journey:
A Heartwarming Story of Courage,
Compassion, and Wisdom

(Book 2 in The Mystic's Gift/Royce Holloway series)

Five years after that glorious week when Maya shared six life-changing principles from an ancient secret book of wisdom with him, Royce is ready for a new chapter—to push his skills and his life to a higher level and make an even greater impact on the world.

In fact, he feels something is *leading* him to do that very thing . . .

So much so, that when Royce's journey takes him to the spectacular, historical Jekyll Island Club Hotel on the Georgia coast, it doesn't surprise him one bit when he "coincidentally" meets a mysterious, well-seasoned world traveler, a traveler whose life was *destined* to intersect with Royce Holloway's—in an unforgettable way for them both.

Join Royce on this powerful, spellbinding trek full of mystics, miracles, and inspirational stories.

You may find your life will never be the same again . . .

The Treasure in Antigua

(Book 3 in The Mystic's Gift/Royce Holloway series)

When Royce Holloway ends up on the magnificent island of Antigua, it's far from a Caribbean vacation. Instead, he finds himself on an incredible journey to locate a sacred, priceless treasure—one that Godfrey Tillman said would deeply impact Royce—and deeply impact the world.

If the carefully hidden prize could ever be found . . .

Along the way, Royce is led through a series of "coincidental" meetings with wise, inspirational mentors from all walks of life, who somehow seem part of a mysterious, bigger plan to guide him in reaching his destination.

Join Royce on his captivating, empowering, and often poignant trek across beautiful Antigua, and as you meet the different teachers on his path, you'll likely find the "student" whose life is changed most . . . is you.

Hidden Jewels of Happiness: Powerful Essays for Finding and Savoring the Gifts on Your Journey

A book of wisdom, encouragement, and empowerment for dealing with life's daily challenges. Let Skip reveal to you the seemingly hidden gifts that are all around us, waiting to be discovered and savored. You'll feel inspired, enlightened, and happier with every page.

Grateful for Everything: Learning, Living, and Loving the Great Game of Life

A deeply engaging book which provides a blueprint for using the power of gratitude to increase your happiness and fulfillment. You'll find delightful stories and practical ideas for turning your life into a great game to play each day, instead of a dreary battle to be fought.

DEDICATION

To Adelyne, Aspen, Boone, and Gatlin

May this book be a priceless resource for each of you on your journey to impact the world through a life of courage, compassion, and generosity. I love you all . . .

TABLE OF CONTENTS

CHAPTER 1

Juliette McKelvey was sprinting.

To make matters worse, she was sprinting . . . while carrying a suitcase.

The scenario pretty much summed up her life to this point. At twenty-eight years old she had been fighting the odds for what seemed like her whole career. Plus, she was *always* playing catch-up—or at least it felt that way.

Now she was doing both as she desperately tried to catch the train pulling out of the station in Belfast, Ireland. It was a train she needed to make, but it looked like it wasn't going to happen—again. Just yesterday, she had missed her flight from New York, forcing her to take the dreaded red-eye from the Big Apple.

Now, history was repeating itself as she frantically raced down the platform.

"No, no, not again!" she shrieked as the train seemed to pull mockingly away before disappearing out of sight. Dropping her suitcase, the agitated young woman grimaced as she stood in the cold with her shoulder-length, wavy black hair wet and frizzy from the thick mist on that late September day.

Shaking her head in disbelief, Juliette picked the luggage back up and began the long walk to the ticket office to see when the next train would leave. She frowned, looking down and seeing how her knee-length paisley dress was now uncomfortably clinging to her petite frame, a result of the combination of perspiration and the damp Irish air.

How did everything go so wrong? she wondered. She wasn't a bad person. Or at least that's what people told her. Well, most people—her parents thought differently, but that was a whole other subject.

Having graduated summa cum laude from college in Pennsylvania, Juliette had enough background and belief in herself to pursue her childhood dream of becoming a journalist. She remembered being glued to the TV into her teens, not in a lazy way like most of her friends, but watching and learning. She was mesmerized by the war correspondents and the women who braved the storms to report on the horrific conditions which people were having to endure everywhere in the world.

Whether it was at Ground Zero, the Golden Gate Bridge, or the Sydney Opera House, the reporters always appeared to be looking into young Juliette's eyes, pleading with her to understand what was happening on the scene.

And those young, brown eyes took it all in. Every day she would watch, and she would grab any object she could use as a microphone, pretending she was *there*. It soon felt like she *was* there, like she was talking with them, not talking to the TV.

That same creativity, passion, and determination which got her through undergraduate years with honors, then got her into the graduate journalism program at the University of Iowa—one of the best in the country. There she focused on international media, and she took her skills to another level. She accepted an internship with *The New York Times*, and she soon showed them they had a superstar on their hands, so they quickly hired her full-time and watched her thrive in a way no other reporter had ever done.

Asia, Africa, Europe, the Caribbean, it didn't matter: wherever they needed a world-class journalist, Juliette McKelvey was the one for the job. People even said she was destined for a Pulitzer Prize.

Her dream had come true.

Until . . .

Until David Marlow came into the picture. He was handsome, talented, and Harvard-educated, and Juliette was flattered when he asked the young reporter to hang out with him after work late one summer afternoon at the prestigious Eastern Shore Club. *What could it hurt?* she thought. He was her new boss, and of course he had her best interest in mind . . . didn't he? Plus, they could get to know each other, and at the end of a long day, a chilled glass of wine would be exactly what the doctor ordered to help her unwind.

So, off they went. Leaving the Times Building in Manhattan and taking a short cab ride to the club seemed so relaxing. Talking with David, she heard about his struggles as he moved across the country—and up the corporate ladder—just like she was doing. "Dog eat dog?" he said with a laugh. "It's more like piranha eat piranha." He spoke of the late nights, the lousy assignments, the terrible bosses, the frustrating and impossible deadlines.

"The time in Capetown, the time in Baghdad, the time in Paris . . ."

Actually, it soon became *annoying* to her. She too had climbed the ladder, and her stories likely could top his in terms of adventure, courage, and determination. But before she could mention anything about that, he quickly cut in.

"But I made it. And I'm only thirty-five years old," he added smugly.

Yes, here he was, the sparkling image of American success—dashing, blonde hair, with a million-dollar smile, and destined to change the media world. He had a corner office, a six-figure salary, and he took calls from celebrities and politicians at his discretion.

He had . . . arrived.

So had the cab that late Thursday afternoon, with the driver walking around, opening the door for Juliette, and tipping his hat. Stepping out, she walked to the front of the car and saw David reaching into his pocket and pulling out a wad of twenty-dollar bills. Not one to be discreet, he conspicuously gave several to the driver.

"Keep the change," he offered with a wide grin.

The driver seemed appreciative. "Thank you as always, Mr. Marlow. Your generosity is second to none."

David smiled in approval and touched Juliette on the shoulder, his hand lingering before pointing her toward the club entrance a few yards away. The place was magnificent. It had beautiful, subtle lighting, perfect landscaping, and every expensive sports car one could think of was parked out front.

"Well, I have to say this isn't quite like Holyfield, Pennsylvania," Juliette laughed.

"Ha, thankfully it's not," he retorted. "I've been to that pit." The snide comment struck a nerve in Juliette. Yes, she was joking when *she* had referred to Holyfield, but it *was* her hometown.

Never mind, she thought. She tucked that thought away along with the one of David having touched her shoulder in a way that was a little *too* comfortable for her at this point.

Entering the establishment after greeting the smiling doorman, David waved to a few male club members as Juliette walked quietly beside him. He seemed to know *everyone*. It was odd; even though she didn't know David well—he had only been with *The Times* a few weeks—the attention they were receiving made her feel important. She thought it was perhaps because her father had always told her she would never make it on her own—she would *need* a man, according to him. She shuddered in disgust at the thought. It was exactly what she promised herself she would never do—depend on someone else—*especially* a man. Though her father died from alcoholism when Juliette was only eighteen, his words of discouragement seemed to always be in the back of her mind. Maybe that was why she was so determined to go to some of those crazy places— Bosnia, Tunisia, Dubai, Bhutan—to constantly prove she needed no one. . .

As the two of them continued down the long, dimly lit hall of the club, she suddenly felt David's hand on her shoulder again—and the touch was even less subtle this time. Surely this wasn't going in *that* direction. No, she would never let that happen. She pulled gently away from him, and he raised an eyebrow. But he composed himself as he gestured toward a room just down the hallway, and as she stepped in, Juliette saw elegant paintings and photographs of distinguished-looking men smoking cigars.

"Former club presidents," he noted aloud. "I'll be there one day. Those old dudes could benefit from some fashion makeovers if you ask me." He laughed arrogantly, then motioned for her to have a seat by him on the only couch in the room—an offer which she quickly rebuffed. She sank into an adjacent opulent, antique-looking chair instead.

Wanting to fill the awkward silence, she commented, "Well, I have to say it's beautiful. But don't we want to sit at the clubhouse bar?"

He shook his head and loosened his tie. "A bunch of cranky old geezers out there. We can have a much better conversation here."

She bunched her eyebrows and looked disapprovingly toward him, and the glare didn't go unnoticed by David Marlow.

"Relax," he said with a smile that made Juliette nervous .

Then it happened.

With one swift move, he had squeezed in uncomfortably beside her. He reached over, grabbed her shoulders, abruptly turned her toward him, and kissed her deeply, *almost violently*. Pulling immediately back, Juliette sneered, "What are you *doing*?"

Ignoring the question, he grabbed Juliette again with both hands and attempted the same thing.

She pushed him firmly away. "Get off me, David!"

Recoiling, he shook his head and scowled. "Guess I should have known. A country girl can't appreciate what's right in front of her. You can take the chick out of the farmland, but . . ."

With a look of contempt, she bolted out of the chair. "You're right, I suppose. I don't know exactly what's in front of me, but what it *seems* is a desperate, disgusting human. I am disappointed, David. I thought you were . . . different. I was looking forward to the days ahead." She picked up her coat and made for the door, tears streaming down both cheeks.

"'Days ahead'?" He shook his head and laughed loudly. "Babe, there'll be no days ahead at this company for you! Don't let the door hit you on the way out of New York—and your career," he shouted sarcastically from the chair.

Juliette turned back and stared into the eyes of the man she thought was her caring boss and potential friend, then she turned away, headed to the front door.

Bypassing the doorman, she hurried over to a barrel-chested cab driver who took one look at her tear-stained face and said, "You okay, ma'am?"

Juliette shook her head. "Fourteen East 43rd Street, please. As quickly as possible."

He nodded and closed the door, and a few seconds later they were off to her apartment, only five minutes away.

Once there, Juliette tipped the cabbie, walked up the short flight of stairs, and opened the door to her place. Stepping inside, she threw her purse against the wall.

What just happened? she thought. *Where will this lead, and what will it do to my career?* Her mind whirled and her stomach dropped at the thought of her dreams for the future.

Just then, a text message lit up her phone. It was David.

Thank goodness, she thought. *He came to his senses, and he is going to apologize.* But would she accept the apology? *No*, she thought. *I'll give him a taste of his own medicine. I'll let him ask me again and again. Then maybe . . .*

Suddenly she saw the words: "Miss McKelvey, your services are no longer needed at *The New York Times*. Aggressive women like yourself who have no concern as to how they are perceived in a business environment such as the Eastern Shore Club have no place in our company. You will receive two weeks' pay, and you are hereby terminated."

Juliette dropped the phone and screamed, "This can't be happening! It can't be! It can't be!"

She fell to the ground, curled up into a fetal position, and began sobbing uncontrollably.

Juliette awoke the next morning, still on the floor in her work clothes. Looking over at the clock, she saw it was 5 a.m. She anxiously grabbed her phone, hoping it was all a horrible dream.

But there it was, the message with the same awful words from the evening before.

Her hands began shaking as thoughts flooded in. *I'll take him to court. Yes, that's exactly what I will do. No, wait, what if I lose? Maybe I—as unthinkable as it is—could go to David's office and beg him not to terminate me?*

She thought back on her young life and blossoming career. All she ever wanted was to be a journalist, making a difference in the world. In one way, David was right—she *was* a naïve girl from the farm. But she had courage and strength and faith.

The question was . . . were those traits going to be enough for her *now*?

CHAPTER 2

Unlike Juliette McKelvey running frantically down the platform earlier, Phillip Westford sat comfortably, sipping from a bottle of water on the day's last train to Cork, which would be departing in about fifteen minutes.

In fact, not only was he *physically* comfortable, now he could say he was *mentally* comfortable . . . or at least more so than he had been in a long, long time.

As he waited on the four o'clock train to leave the station on that blustery day, his thoughts drifted back over the last few years. There were the miserable years after winning the lottery, but then . . . there were the recent events that had transformed him—in a powerful, glorious way that few people could ever understand.

Even to him, it seemed so odd to think that way. After all, what person in their right mind would find that winning two hundred and fifty million dollars could ever have any connection with a life of *misery*?

But for Phillip, that is exactly what it had been—misery.

Modestly dressed in a pair of faded blue jeans, a light green sweater, and camel-colored suede boots, he certainly didn't stand out as a lottery winner—and that's exactly how he wanted it—low-key, like the "good old days." He thought back over the many years with his now ex-wife. High school sweethearts, they had promised each other they would be together in sickness and in health. But what about through the challenges of . . . wealth?

Now he was fifty-one years old, sitting on a train heading out of Belfast, *without* the one woman he thought would always be by his side. Yes, those days were gone. Long gone.

But even so, Phillip was excited about what was waiting for him at the end of this great ride through a country he had heard so much about. He was fully prepared and supremely grateful for the opportunity he was being given—to add what undoubtedly would be the final layer of happiness onto his new life.

Because now, at last, he knew the secret . . . and he would break the wretched curse, once and for all.

Phillip's thoughts were interrupted as he saw a disheveled, yet attractive young woman climb into the train car, seating herself directly across from him.

Noting the surprised look on his face, she quickly commented, "I know. I'm a mess." She sighed and wiped the windblown hair out of her face.

Phillip laughed and ran his fingers through his freshly cut, sandy blonde hair. "Well, if you don't mind me saying so, it looks as if you could use a drink."

"Well, I don't typically accept drinks from strangers on Irish trains, but in this case . . . 'for sure,'" she replied with a grin.

Phillip raised a curious eyebrow and replied, "Um, I'll take that as a compliment . . . I *think*?"

She laughed. "Okay, that didn't come out quite right. So, yes, thank you. A glass of wine would be therapeutic at this point."

A waiter came by dressed in a perfectly pressed uniform—black slacks and a white long-sleeved shirt with a red bow tie. Phillip held up two fingers and said, "Two glasses of wine, please, my good man. Clos Du Val Cabernet, if you have it."

The young, red-haired man looked at Phillip and replied in a soft Irish accent, "Absolutely, sir. I shall have them in one moment."

Phillip Westford nodded and smiled, and Juliette found she was smiling too.

"Yes, that's exactly what I need." She took a breath and said, "I'm Juliette."

Phillip grinned and shook her outstretched hand. "I'm Phillip. Where are you coming from?"

"Well, I guess you could say I'm coming from craziness. Or maybe that's where I'm headed."

Phillip threw back his head and laughed. "Well, I'm trusting this train is headed to *happiness*, although it may stop at craziness along the way. I've been there also, so I'm sure I'll recognize it."

Juliette chuckled. "I'm actually from Des Moines. I'm a reporter, and I'm headed down near Cork to cover a story. I was supposed to catch a flight straight to Cork after a layover in New York, but I missed it. So . . . the next best thing I could do, unfortunately, was catch a flight into Belfast and then a train down to the southern part of the country. Then I missed my train earlier, and I'm lucky to have even gotten a seat on this one, which is the last of the day as you probably know. How about you?"

Phillip smiled and replied, "I'm eventually headed to a town outside of Cork, as I've got a little unfinished business there. I'm also coming from New York, but I flew to Belfast intentionally so I could take in the Irish scenery along the way since it's my first visit. I understand it's about five hours to get to Cork."

Juliette nodded, and just then the waiter returned with their glasses of wine. Once he set the drinks down, the two patrons thanked him, to which he smiled and replied cheerfully, "My pleasure!" before walking briskly away.

Juliette thought for a moment before she spoke again. "It seems odd. I was supposed to catch the flight from JFK, which I missed. Then I was supposed to catch the train a couple of hours ago, which I missed. Now I ended up on this train, which for some reason, I already feel like I was supposed to be on after all."

Phillip smiled. "Maybe so. Hopefully, it's the luck of the Irish already working for you."

"Cheers to that," she offered with a smile as she raised her glass toward Phillip.

"Cheers," Phillip responded as he grinned and raised his glass to hers.

As the train began pulling out of the station, both travelers looked out the window and noticed how gloomy and wet the surroundings were. "A true British day I guess," Phillip said with a laugh.

"Just like I've heard," Juliette agreed. "This is my first time to Ireland also, but my grandmother is Irish through and through—O'Quinn was her name—and she used to tell me about the dreadful weather here."

"Looks like she was right," he offered. "I can already tell this is quite different from my little hometown."

"Where's that, if you don't mind me asking?"

"Not at all. I'm from Springfield, Missouri—just a wee bit west of here," he said in his best Irish dialect.

Juliette raised an eyebrow. "You'll need to work on that accent a bit."

Phillip smiled, then took a sip of his wine and inquired, "By the way, what did you tell me you would be writing about near Cork?"

"Well, I didn't say, but if you must know, my editor is Irish, and he sent me here to cover a silly story about a rumor he heard." She rolled her eyes.

Phillip laced his fingers together and put them behind his head as he leaned back in his seat.

Juliette went on, "There is supposedly a guy from America who is giving away some money from winning the lottery years ago. It's a secret as far as exactly what he's going to do with the money, but according to what my boss heard, it will likely happen in a town just outside Cork. My job is to track the guy down and interview him."

Juliette then shook her head and grumbled, "I was a war correspondent in some of the most amazing places you could imagine, and now I am relegated to being told by an Iowa newspaper editor to track down a gazillionaire who's giving a little money away."

"You never know," Phillip replied. "Sometimes the best stories come from the least obvious places."

"Maybe," she replied. "What's ironic is I'm so off schedule, I've probably already screwed this up. I missed my flight, missed my train, and now I'm hundreds of miles away from Cork, close to deadline, and I have no idea where to find this guy."

"Hmm." Phillip said casually, "You're right, that doesn't sound too promising. What's the gentleman's name?"

"Phil," she replied quickly. At that moment, Juliette paused as the color slowly drained from her face.

"Wait. Did you say your name was . . . Phillip?"

"Has been for fifty-one years," he said with a smile.

"You're not by any chance. . ."

Phillip cocked his head and smiled. "Maybe. . ."

"Oh my gosh . . . you're Phil Westford? *Yes*, you are—I recognize you now!"

"At your service. By the way, I prefer *Phillip*, if you don't mind. The press keeps calling me Phil—and it's annoying." He laughed.

She shook her head as she fumbled for words. "Oh my, I'm sorry, I just didn't . . . I mean, what are the odds?"

Phillip sipped his wine, then grinned, obviously enjoying her backpedaling. "As I said, some of the best stories come from the least obvious places . . ."

"So," she continued, "is it true that you're giving away like a million dollars of your winnings?"

"No," he replied curtly and with a sly smile.

"No?" she echoed.

"I'm giving away, well, let's just say . . . more than that. I have one hundred and one million dollars left at this point, so I have some options." Phillip chuckled.

Juliette's eyes grew wide. "I can't even fathom that."

Phillip shrugged. "Well, there was a lot more, but I was 'asked' to give half to my former spouse."

"Your *former* spouse? I'm sorry."

"Thank you. The divorce was terrible, but that's a story for another day. As far as the winnings, honestly, I haven't touched the lottery money since we split up. Before the divorce, I splurged a little. But since the divorce, I've been living off my pre-lottery savings—which I can do for quite a few more years if need be. I know it must sound odd, but I still cringe when I think about using any of the lottery money because of the chaos it created in my life—the lottery curse, I guess you could say."

Juliette nodded. "I've heard of the curse, for sure. If it's been that bad, living off something besides the lottery winnings sounds like a good idea—if you can do that for a while."

She noticed Phillip was looking away, shaking his head. "It's been a curse alright. There have been so many people I believed I could trust, but the judgments, the misunderstandings, the backstabbings . . . they have been unthinkable. However, I'm hoping this curse will soon be broken—for good."

His curious statement made Juliette pause, but when Phillip didn't elaborate, she added, "I've also been through some things over the past year which have made me realize that finding people you can trust is difficult. I have felt so unappreciated and discouraged. Sometimes it seems to be more than I can bear, and I think about how to get out of all this mess . . . into a new career . . ."

Juliette put her head in her hands and began softly sobbing.

Phillip, now feeling empathy with this young woman's plight, sat calmly for a few seconds, then leaned forward and gently said, "Juliette."

She raised her head and looked at him with teary eyes.

Phillip continued, "I don't know what happened to you, but it was obviously traumatic. However, I will suggest that you cannot quit when you are so close . . ."

Juliette furrowed her brow in confusion while Phillip sat in silence as if carefully measuring his next sentence.

"I mean so close to greatness."

"Phillip, what are you talking about?" she said, shaking her head.

"You came to interview me, right?"

Juliette nodded slowly.

"Well, people ask me for interviews constantly, but what I am about to tell you, I have never told anyone, and I doubt I will ever repeat it. I will share with you my entire journey that led me to be on this train—and why I mentioned a few moments ago the destination for me will hopefully be happiness. Juliette, once you hear this, you'll never be the same person again. Plus," he said with a grin, "I bet you'll have some loyal new fans out there in Iowa. Deal?"

"Yes, it's a deal," she replied evenly as she wiped her eyes.

Phillip grinned, attempting to lighten the mood. "Great, because I guess you could say I'm a 'recovering lottery winner,' so telling my story to you will be therapeutic for me."

Although she didn't know it then, Juliette McKelvey was about to hear a tale unlike anything her journalism background could ever have prepared her for . . .

CHAPTER 3

Juliette couldn't believe what she had just heard. "I don't know how to thank you—I am so grateful. I'm not sure I even know what to say . . ."

Raising his hand to stop her, Phillip shook his head. "Let's start with you. How did you end up in Des Moines?"

The young woman lowered her eyes. "Well, it's not particularly my dream job, but quite frankly, I am happy to have any job in the field right now."

Phillip's puzzled look urged her to continue.

Juliette quietly said, "It's still so hard for me to talk about . . ."

"Then don't," Phillip reassured her.

"No, no. I feel I can trust you, Phillip, and although I feel vulnerable talking about it, I would like to tell you."

Phillip nodded and smiled.

Juliette began sharing the story of her upbringing and then talked about the stint at *The Times* and how it all ended so tragically.

"I never in my wildest dreams thought harassment would happen to me. I mean, I was a hard-core correspondent for years. I thought I was prepared . . ."

Her voice trailed off, and Phillip looked at her compassionately. "We never know what life will bring to us—or take away. However, everything that happens in our lives is for our ultimate good, if we can believe that."

Juliette looked at him, pessimistic. "I have heard that before, but . . . I am just not sure I believe it. How do you *know* it's true? I mean, David Marlow ruined my career—maybe even my life. I'm a reporter in Des Moines, Iowa now, remember?"

Phillip shook his head. "Right now, you are in the beautiful country of Ireland. In fact, not only are you in Ireland, but you are also traveling through the Irish countryside with a man seated opposite you who is most likely going to give you the story of a lifetime. It's a story that will not only affect *you*, but it will impact people who read your work all over the world. Your career and your life are far from ruined. By the way, you wouldn't have ended up here with me if you hadn't been working in Des Moines." He smiled broadly.

"It sounds amazing, but do you really think that's true? I so want to believe it all."

"I *know* it's true," he said with a reassuring smile. "Now I'm sure as a reporter, you have a voice recorder, so I suggest you get it out, turn it on, then sit back and relax. We don't have much time until we get to Cork."

Juliette smiled in a noticeably more comfortable way, took a sip of her wine, and then reached in her purse. Producing a small recorder, she turned it to "ON" and placed it on the table between them as Phillip began speaking . . .

"My wife, Chloe, and I had been married for twenty years. With a nice home, a comfortable income, and two healthy children, I felt like life couldn't get any better.

"One night we were out with friends, and they suggested we play the lottery. I had never played before and didn't particularly care if I ever played, but Chloe encouraged me and said it was 'just for kicks and giggles.'

"The ticket cost ten dollars."

Juliette looked at him with astonishment. "What was the number you chose?"

Phillip laughed. "Well, that's probably the question I get the most. It was a combination of my wife's birth date, my daughter's age at that time, and our telephone number at the first house we lived in."

Juliette shook her head. "Unbelievable. I can't imagine the odds."

Phillip raised an eyebrow and quipped, "It was 5,678,227 to one, if you'd like to know precisely."

She laughed.

"But that day," he continued, "I guess the odds were 100 percent in my favor. After purchasing the ticket at a convenience store, I threw it onto the dashboard of my car. As luck would have it, we went around a curve that night, and the ticket must have slipped off the dashboard and landed between the seat and the door—I never even noticed it was gone."

Juliette nodded and leaned in as Phillip carried on. "Three days later, I was cleaning out my car and came across the ticket. I picked it up and threw it into a little paper sack, along with all the other 'junk' that had accumulated; with two kids, a lot of things somehow end up in Dad's car." He laughed.

"I took the small bag and put it into the trash can in our garage, and I didn't think anything about it until dinnertime. During the meal, Chloe asked where the ticket was, and I said without thinking, 'Out with the rest of the trash.' I wasn't sure if she was angry or not, but she retorted, 'Never mind, I'll get it myself. I had a good feeling about that ticket.'

"I just shook my head as she walked out to the garage. A few moments later, she walked back inside the house with a stunned look on her face. I asked her, 'What's wrong? Are you okay?' I thought she had been bitten by a spider or something in the garage.

"She looked at me quietly and simply said, 'Phillip, we won the lottery.' Of course, I assumed she was teasing me, so I went back to enjoying my meal.

"Just then, with a dazed look I'll never forget, she laid down the newspaper from two days before. My eyes fell to the paper. The results were circled with a pencil, and she looked at me and firmly said, 'Phillip, take the ticket, and I am going to read these winning numbers to you from the newspaper.' As she got to the last two numbers, I was shaking. '4 . . . 7.'

"We both started crying. That jackpot was a record two hundred and fifty million dollars. We had won a new life."

Juliette sat mesmerized as Phillip paused and looked up, seemingly lost in thought. "In hindsight, we won a new life, but not one I would wish on anyone."

He looked out the window as Juliette asked softly, "Phillip, what happened? What happened that turned this from such a glorious event to . . . whatever it became?"

Phillip shook his head and quietly mimicked her words. "'To whatever it became' . . . exactly.

"At first, life was like most people would imagine for a lottery winner. We traveled, bought a beautiful new home, and gave interviews to the media about how wonderful our lives were with all this new money. We were celebrities. But then . . ." Phillip's words trailed off as he reminisced.

Juliette sat quietly, waiting patiently for him to continue.

Regaining his focus, Phillip added, "Chloe had come from a poor family—not that mine was wealthy—but her early years were ones of constant financial struggle. After the lottery win, she seemed to let money define who she was. She started spending more and more, and after a few months, she began making irrational plans for what she wanted us to do with the money. She wanted a bigger home. She wanted more cars. We had hired the best lawyer in the country—one that helped people deal with sudden influxes of wealth, but soon Chloe decided she didn't want to listen to him. In fact, she demanded I fire him because he was 'after our money.' She became increasingly unreasonable and even paranoid."

Juliette interjected, "I have heard things like this can happen with sudden wealth."

"Yes," Phillip replied somberly. "I would never have believed it would happen to her, but now, I assure you it can happen to anyone. Then, within months, I began noticing changes in the way my wife treated the children. At that time, they were only in their mid-teens, and we had always prided ourselves on how well adjusted and kind they were. But then . . . Chloe began buying them lavish gifts and started insisting they wear expensive clothes. They, of course, were still impressionable adolescents, and now they had all this money thrust upon them, so it was a recipe for disaster. When I tried to step in and remind all three of them about our family's values and the priority of making a difference in the lives of others, my wife chided me—often in front of them."

Juliette nodded. "I remember my father and mother did not support each other in family decisions, and it led to horrible stress on us all."

"Exactly," Phillip said, shaking his head. "So, add in this crazy amount from the lottery win, and you can imagine how combustible the environment became. Chloe and I began fighting bitterly—something I never dreamed would happen. All the while, she was spending exorbitantly. Then, to my utter disbelief, she got involved in drugs when the spending frenzies didn't bring her the happiness she hoped they would."

Juliette covered her mouth in shock.

"One day I found a massive number of amphetamines in her cabinet in the bathroom. When I quizzed her about it, she not only slammed the cabinet door shut, but she also slapped me in a way that was full of rage. I looked into her eyes and realized I no longer knew who she was. It was the beginning of the end, and I knew it."

Juliette looked sympathetically at Phillip. "I am so sorry. I just can't imagine. What about your children?"

Phillip's expression became subdued. "I haven't talked with them in over a year. My children meant more to me than anything, and now they are turned against me. Chloe made sure of that. We decided it was time to divorce, and the subsequent legal proceedings were horrible, as you can imagine. Every day, Chloe gave my children her perspective on what had happened in the courtroom. It was never anything but angry, negative comments about me—and it was all untrue."

Juliette shook her head in disbelief and continued to listen intently as Phillip finished. "I guess some people would say I 'won' because I received half of the money, and I was free of what had sadly become a miserable marriage. But I would say differently. I would say neither of us won. The lawyers were probably the only true winners . . . and at that point, I became a broken, angry man."

Juliette sighed. "It's just unthinkable that money can do that to a family. Something that has so much potential for good can end up causing so much . . . bad."

Phillip nodded. "I haven't seen Chloe or my children since the last day in court. The kids have said they never want to see me again, and since they are now of legal age to choose, I am guessing they never will . . ."

The two sat quietly for a moment, then Juliette broke the silence. "Did *anything* good come out of this whole sordid mess in the end?"

For the first time since he began the story, a smile flickered across Phillip Westford's face. "Juliette, this is where the story becomes, well . . . unbelievable." Shaking his head, Phillip added, "At least, I know *I* would never have believed it—if it hadn't happened to me . . ."

CHAPTER 4

The train was gliding through the Irish countryside, and the conductor walked past the passenger cabins, holding up his pocket watch and declaring to anyone who cared to listen, "Three hours to Cork! Three hours to Cork!" The waiter stopped by and refilled the wine glasses of the two travelers, and Juliette sat back as Phillip continued his saga.

"It's been three years since we hit the jackpot, and I now live in Manhattan. I'm not a 'big city' person, but I wanted to get as far away from all the lottery hassle as I could. New York seemed a good option after trying several other states and becoming increasingly discouraged with my life. Every day was filled with guilt, loneliness, and regret, and I had no idea how to escape what seemed like a downward spiral toward full-blown depression.

"I often sat and wondered how I could go from having a wonderfully simple life to having it ruined almost overnight by too much money. It didn't make sense, but that was my new normal, and I was not adjusting well at all.

"My apartment faces Central Park, and two weeks ago I looked out my window and saw an older man in a light brown trench coat sitting on a bench feeding the pigeons. He looked so content that watching him just affirmed how unhappy I was. For whatever reason, I wanted to go down and talk with him, so I put on my coat and gloves—it was a gloomy, cold day in the city, and I still remember it perfectly.

"As I approached the bench he was sitting on, the man looked up at me with the most magnificent, disarming smile. He was thin-framed, and his fair skin and sparkling green eyes added to his gentle presence. Tipping his tweed Irish flat cap, revealing a full head of red hair, he gestured to the empty spot on the bench. 'Have a seat, my friend.'

"It was strange because at that point, it occurred to me I was living in this huge city, and I had no friends—so his words were comforting.

"'Don't mind if I do,' I responded back gratefully.

"Right then, the man looked into my eyes as if he knew me and said, 'Young man, what are you searching for?'

"It totally caught me off guard, and I didn't know how to respond. 'Um, maybe just a little peace,' I fumbled.

"He nodded, paused, and then replied as if he saw right through my remark. 'Well, you won't find it here, I'm afraid.'

"I thought he was telling me he had changed his mind and now wanted to be by himself, so I quickly offered, 'Oh, no problem, I can sit somewhere else—these benches are a little small anyway.'

"He touched me on the arm as if he were reaching deep into my soul, then he shook his head and replied with a smile, 'This bench is exactly where you should be right now. But just for now.'

"'What?' I stammered. Confused and slightly annoyed, I replied, 'So is there a time limit on the city benches?'

"The man laughed and shook his head. 'Sit here for as long as you'd like—but you won't find peace. Maybe someday you'll find sitting on a park bench will do the trick for you, but at this point I believe you'll need to take a little journey to find the tranquility you're looking for. It's not in New York.'

"Wondering what I had stumbled into, I rolled my eyes and replied, 'What are you talking about? Sir, the *trip* I have been on for the last three years has brought me anything but peace. I think I'm through traveling. Sitting here with you and the pigeons is really about the only kind of peace I want to find. By the way, I don't even know your name—and why would you think I need to go anywhere else? With all due respect, you don't know me.'

"The man leaned back and adjusted his cap. 'The name is Patrick O'Rourke—from Dublin. And I know you better than you might think, Mr. Westford. You *definitely* need a journey—especially one with the tour guides I know.' He smiled knowingly.

"'How did you know my name?' Now I was really getting worked up. 'Are you a stupid reporter—or some paparazzi? I mean, how . . .'

"But he had touched my arm again and I felt that same calm energy as before. Then, laughing a wonderful, charming Irish laugh, he said, 'Rest assured I'm no reporter. And as far as paparazzi, I can't even spell the word—plus I don't own a camera.' Then his countenance became more serious. 'How I know these things are not important, and as far as the trek I am proposing—it's one I've also been on, and like you, I didn't want to go. But I did, and I have been a different man ever since.'

"Bewildered, I responded, 'Okay, I've never met you—in fact, I've never even *seen* you until today—but you're telling me I should go on some journey.'

"Patrick O'Rourke crossed his arms, leaned back, then looked at me and smiled. 'Yep, I think that's about right. Oh, it will mean traveling across the world, and it could be a bit dangerous.'"

Recalling that moment, Phillip said to Juliette, "I just shook my head and said, 'Well, as far as danger, the journey I have been on for the last couple of years has been about as treacherous as they get.'

"'I suppose you're right. Money sometimes does strange things to folks,' Patrick added.

"I shook my head again and blurted out, 'There's no way you could know about that if you don't know who I am. What are you, like my guardian angel or something? If so, you've been sleeping on the job for a while.'

"Patrick O'Rourke grinned and shrugged. 'What I *do* know is where you have been because I too have been there, and I believe the look in your eyes is from the burden you carry. It's my gift to know these things, and it's a gift I do not take for granted. It was part of the healing I received along the way. As far as being your guardian angel . . . well,' he said with a wink, 'who knows?' Patrick paused, scanned the area, and looked pensively back at me. 'Now, my friend, the pigeons are flying away, the shadows are falling, and my time here is short. Are you ready? You can certainly say no, although I wouldn't recommend it.' He chuckled.

"When Patrick saw me hesitate, he reached into the inside pocket of his trench coat and pulled out a crumpled note. He put it in the right breast pocket of *my* coat and said with a grin, 'I think I need a little coffee.' With that, the older man stood up, stretched, and headed over to a small coffee stand about twenty yards away. I reached into my pocket, taking out and unfolding the note he had given me. Three names were written on the paper: Ahmet, José, and David.

"As I glanced over my shoulder, I saw Patrick had purchased two coffees and was headed back to sit down with me. Looking up and away from him, I suppose I gave the appearance I was trying to find divine guidance for the significance of the three names as Patrick sat down on the bench and laughed.

"'Well, I'm sure the heavens *do* know who belongs to those names, but it's probably easier for me just to tell you.'

"I grinned at the absurdity of the situation. 'Okay, and since you may be my guardian angel, are these like the Three Wise Men?'

"Patrick shrugged nonchalantly and smiled. 'Something like that. Ahmet Mansour lives outside of Cairo, Egypt. José Gonzalez lives in the jungle of southeastern Mexico, and David Cairns lives in the mountains of Colorado—probably the most northern part of Colorado.'

"'Wow,' I responded in surprise, 'those are quite different places.'

"Patrick took a sip of his coffee, then handed a cup to me and said, 'Well, they are quite different people. All amazing, however. In fact, that's probably the common denominator—they are amazing people. Like you—and me—they were each a seeker.'

"Still a bit suspicious, I raised an eyebrow and looked down at the steaming java Patrick had brought me. 'Thank you for the coffee—black, just how I like it. But Patrick . . . how do you know these men?' I asked. 'I mean, where did you meet them if they live in different parts of the world?'

"The old man rubbed his chin. 'I guess when you are supposed to meet people, you just meet them. Different folks add different elements of value to your life, depending on what you need, and they will simply arrive—if you are open to that kind of stuff.' Patrick gave me a big smile and took another sip of his coffee."

Phillip looked at Juliette and noted, "For some reason, I had now gone beyond wondering how Patrick had ended up in my life. I just *knew* it was supposed to be that way. But what I *did* want to know was how the names on the crumpled piece of paper were going to fit into my life—if at all."

Juliette leaned in as Phillip went on, "'Okay, here's the thing, Patrick: the thought of going around the world to meet these people does seem kind of nuts when I don't know them—or *you* for that matter. But oddly, something inside me says I need to go, and I can't figure out why that is.'

"Patrick leaned back again and spoke quietly as he looked off into the distance. 'I was like you, Phillip—more than you realize. But being with these three men, disparate as they are, led me on a path to healing and to a new life. I didn't know what I was searching for—but they somehow knew exactly what I needed. I have no doubt they are three of the wisest people in the world. What they have learned and what they will willingly share with you will change you—and bring the contentment you desire.'"

Phillip looked at Juliette and shook his head. "I realized my jaw had fallen open, and I couldn't help it."

Juliette laughed. "I don't blame you! This is incredible—keep going, Phillip."

"'Patrick, come on,' I chided him. 'Three of the wisest people in the world? Really? Well, I'll have to be the judge of that, but I will say this: somehow, I trust you about this whole journey thing. I feel as if you do know what I have gone through—whether you know the exact details or not. If these people can help me—and it sounds like they can—I am willing to go on this trek. Plus,' I added with a grin, 'Who wouldn't want to travel to Cairo?'

"Patrick smiled. 'Let me tell you a little more about where you'll be going. These are not, shall we say, your typical resort towns.'

"I took another sip of coffee and turned more toward him, listening carefully as he continued.

"'To get to my friends in the Mexican jungle, the mountains of Colorado, and the desert of Egypt, I'll have someone meet you at each airport—they will guide you safely to your destination.'

"'Guides? Wow, sounds like quite a challenging trek, for sure.' I laughed.

"Patrick shrugged and said with a grin, 'I think you'll find this journey easier than the lottery path you've been on.'

"He sipped his coffee as I shook my head in disbelief.

"'Okay, Patrick, I'm hooked,' I said with a smile. 'When do I start this adventure?'

"Patrick rubbed his chin thoughtfully and replied, 'Meet me at my home tonight at eight o'clock. We'll have dinner, and I will provide you with all the details.' He handed me another small piece of paper on which was written *28 Lexington Ave.*

"I looked at the address and tucked the paper into my pocket as we stood and shook hands."

Just then, Phillip turned to look at Juliette and said, "As I stood there looking into Patrick's compassionate eyes, I somehow knew he was right—my life was never going to be the same."

At that moment, Juliette looked down at her forearms and saw the goosebumps rising . . .

CHAPTER 5

Peering out the window, Juliette noticed the train was entering a densely wooded area. She spotted a large golden eagle flying effortlessly overhead into the forest ahead of them.

"We're *all* on a journey, aren't we, Phillip?" She smiled, still admiring the eagle.

He glanced up, caught sight of the majestic bird, and agreed. "No doubt about it. I think you and I both understand that." He paused, and once the eagle passed out of sight, he asked, "Juliette, tell me, do you ever regret not taking David Marlow to court over the harassment incident?"

She shrugged. "Rarely. One thing my father *did* teach me when I was younger was that life will unfold much better without resistance from us. 'Don't force anything,' he would say. I thought it was a lot of nonsense, but later I realized those were words of faith. It made me believe that down deep, my dad was a good man, doing the best he could—he was just often misguided. However, his instruction about life unfolding was a gift I am grateful for. It has saved me a lot of guilt and regret when I remind myself to follow that philosophy."

Phillip nodded in approval.

At that moment, the train entered a short tunnel in the forest, and the passengers were thrown into darkness, making Juliette gasp. Seconds later, as the train passed through to the other side, she looked at Phillip and said sheepishly, "Guess I'm not as brave as I would like to be."

"Even after this short time with you, I can tell that you are one of the most courageous women I have ever met," Phillip responded with a smile. "We all get scared of the unknown sometimes—I know *I* do."

Relieved, Juliette returned her focus to the story. "So let me ask *you* something, Phillip. Why *do* you think Mr. O'Rourke ended up in your life that day?"

"Looking back, I know exactly why he was there. But it's not for the reason you might think . . ."

Juliette cocked her head, then glanced down to make sure the voice recorder was getting every word as Phillip continued his extraordinary story.

"I went back to my apartment, and strangely enough, I questioned myself on whether or not I should go to Patrick's residence. In my heart, I felt I would, but I couldn't help but wonder how this mysterious story would end. I knew the only way to find out was to see him that evening. Plus, at that point in my life, I still had so much sadness and bitterness about losing my wife and children that I was desperate to move forward, and I hoped this was the next step. As your dad said, I needed to 'let life unfold'. . ."

Juliette smiled and nodded her agreement as Phillip carried on.

"When I got to Patrick's address that evening, I walked up three flights of stairs in a nondescript brown brick high-rise—easily one hundred years old—and I was amazed by what I saw when he opened the door. The inside was impeccable, as though I had walked into an exquisite Irish museum. The feeling, the light, the Queen Ann furniture, all had such a distinctly British feel. It was elegant.

"Patrick noticed my admiring gaze and smiled as if he knew what I was thinking. 'I planned it that way. It reminds me of Dublin—my home in Ireland.'

"I nodded. 'I can imagine.'

"As he led me through the place, I noticed a small table in the den. It was a handsome antique cherry piece, and adorning it was a gold-framed picture of a beautiful woman, likely in her mid-thirties.

"'Patrick, who is she?' I asked gently.

"'My wife, Lenora. She died many years ago. She was the love of my life. And then . . .'

"Patrick's voice trailed off, and I decided to carry the conversation. 'What a lovely woman.'

"He nodded in agreement. 'Yes, inside, and out. Her death is what started me on my own journey, Phillip. So even though our struggles have been different, they are in many ways the same, as I said.'"

At that point, Juliette noted Phillip's distant look as he said, "I realized then that Patrick really *did* understand the pain I felt. It also seemed that I, for the first time in years, was allowing myself to feel that same pain without fear of judgment."

Juliette nodded her compassionate understanding, and Phillip continued.

"Patrick smiled as he looked at the picture, and he seemed to be reminiscing about his days with Lenora. Then, as if he realized his thoughts had drifted, he turned and motioned for me to come to the table. 'I hope you like roast beef and potatoes.'

"'My favorite,' I replied as I took a seat. 'This takes me back to my home in Missouri. My mom cooked the best roast beef and potatoes anywhere.' Patrick smiled, and after we sat down, he bowed his head and offered a Gaelic blessing over the meal. When he finished, I raised my head and said softly, 'That was beautiful, Patrick.'

"Patrick nodded his approval. 'Thank you, my friend. I now know gratitude is one of the most important traits a person can have.'"

Phillip then said to Juliette, "Something about those words struck me deeply. I wanted to learn more about his comment, but before I could ask, Patrick started sharing what turned out to be some touching and uncannily accurate words for my situation . . .

"'Phillip, you lost your wife through divorce, and I lost mine through death. Which is worse, well, I don't know. But I do know there is enormous pain in both of our scenarios—pain that others don't understand unless they have been through something like we dealt with.' I nodded in agreement, as I had often thought the same. Both situations are about separation from someone you loved, and both situations contain an extraordinary amount of sadness. Patrick elaborated as we started on the wonderful meal he had prepared. His words touched my heart . . .

"'Meeting Lenora was the best thing that ever happened to me,' Patrick began. 'We married a little later in life, and we were grateful we had finally found each other. I was in the Irish military, and at that time, I had gone back to school and was studying religion at the university, with hopes of becoming a priest. But even though I was in school, when the war broke out, I was sent into combat and we quickly realized we would have to reevaluate our plans. Then shortly before I left for my tour of duty, we found out Lenora was pregnant, which was a miracle for us—we were elated.

"'She was a nurse, and when I left, she stayed back in Dublin and worked at a hospital. I wish she hadn't, but at the time, we needed the money. When I left, she wrote me every day, and every day I wrote her back. We talked about our family and raising our child—

which we soon found out was a boy. The letters were what sustained me in some of the darkest hours, in the times when I saw things no one should ever have to see. I couldn't wait to get home to her—and to our forthcoming son.

"'Then one Saturday, the letters stopped, and I had no idea why. Two days later, my commander called me to his office and told me he had just gotten word that Lenora had died. She had gone into labor far too early. Somehow, she was able to drive herself to the hospital, but she began hemorrhaging, and within a few hours, my wife and our unborn child were gone.' Patrick had tears welling up in his eyes as he added, 'They said the last words she uttered were, "I love you, Patrick." To this day, I can't get the image out of my mind . . .'

"Patrick sat up straight and commented, 'I guess in some way, I don't really *want* to get the picture out of my mind—that picture of her saying she loved me.'"

Phillip stopped the conversation and wiped away tears as Juliette sat quietly, absorbing every word. Phillip gently added, "Then Patrick said, 'That's when I knew my life had been turned upside down. I didn't know what to do next, but I knew it was all going to be different.

"'The army gave me a bereavement leave so I could attend the funeral and take some time away to try and recover from the awful events. It was during that period that I met Ahmet Mansour.'"

Phillip looked at Juliette, and noticed her gaze had become quizzical, as if she was searching for an answer. "You know, one of the 'Three Wise Men,'" he reminded her.

Juliette smiled and nodded as Phillip added, "I was puzzled too because I couldn't see where this connection with Ahmet could possibly come from. But I was about to find out . . .

"'Ahmet Monsour is a remarkable man,' Patrick said admirably. 'Though he lived in Dublin, Ahmet was originally from Cairo, and he was tall, handsome, and self-assured. He was teaching at the University of Dublin, and he was also a participant in a support meeting I was attending for people dealing with grief. Ahmet had gone through a trauma when he was younger, and even though he had healed to a great extent, he still understood the value of this kind of therapy, so he joined us often. When I met him at the first session I attended, even though I was a bit reserved, we became immediate friends. Having been through his own struggles, he could relate to the pain I had been through. After that initial meeting, he approached me and offered, "Patrick, I can tell God has given you a gift for making a difference in people's lives. You don't fully see that now, but you will one day, and this tragedy you have gone through will eventually allow you to be able to serve others at a new level."'

"Patrick continued, 'I stood there, shocked by Ahmet's words, wondering where this intuition of his had come from. But even though his comments seemed genuine, and I believed him, I didn't talk with Ahmet anymore about this short conversation until much later in my recovery process. I attended the gatherings, became more engaged, and soon realized what a wise man my new Egyptian friend was when it came to dealing with life—and death.

"After twelve weeks, thanks in great part to his encouragement, I was able to leave the sessions and go back to the military, and I was stationed in Dublin as a chaplain. Although I occasionally traveled to spend time with our troops around the world, I was mostly in Ireland, helping soldiers returning home to deal with their own grief—it was the perfect position for me.

"'In the meantime, Ahmet and I became close friends. We met every week for coffee, and he continued to share his wisdom. For some reason, he also valued *my* wisdom, and our conversations became special to both of us. Later, David Cairns, a brilliant, kindhearted world traveler from Colorado, would move to Dublin and become part of our group of friends. The three of us came to understand that we each had unique gifts, but the common denominator was a desire to learn, grow, and make the world a better place. Odd as it may sound, it truly seemed God brought us together through our tragedies and our lessons learned, and we all felt led to combine our strengths to serve humanity.'

"I couldn't help but blurt out to Patrick, 'It doesn't sound odd to me at all. It sounds like you all had lots in common, but it also seems like each person's background brought diversity into your collaboration. A perfect fit!'

"Patrick nodded and smiled at my enthusiasm. 'Yes, that's true. Diversity of skill, coupled with a common cause, can lead to great power.' He went on, 'We began sharing our collective thoughts with the world through writing. We wrote some books individually and many books together, plus we wrote a few under a variety of pen names. Writing was therapeutic for us, and we sold millions of copies as people began gravitating toward our ideas. Many spiritual or self-help classics you know today were written by one of us under those pen names—books that people have said changed their lives. Later, we even started a special little consulting company together, which is when José joined us. I'll tell you about that some other time.' Patrick smiled."

At that moment, Juliette was acutely aware of the soft, lulling effect the rocking of the train was having on her as it went *click, click, click* down the tracks, passing through the quaint Irish villages. Her mind drifted, and her senses became overwhelmed by the beauty of the surroundings and a deep feeling of gratitude as she thought about this special time with Phillip Westford. She found herself weighing the possibility that all the horrible things she had gone through in New York— and the terribly boring times over the last year in Des Moines—truly *were* preparing her for this magnificent trek through Ireland with Phillip.

She thought back on her days in college and how she had dreamed of covering exciting stories—wars, blizzards, rescues, all sorts of events that shape the world. But it never crossed her mind there was a chance she could meet someone like Phillip, poised to impact the world in a way she still could scarcely comprehend. In their brief time together, she was already learning from him about life—*so much* about life. It felt as if her deep pain was being healed by a man who had studied under some of the greatest spiritual teachers.

Yes, *healing* was exactly what she was feeling . . .

After what seemed hours, though it was likely only seconds, Phillip broke the silence as he noticed Juliette's distant look. "Forgive me, Juliette, if this all sounds like nonsense. We can stop at any time . . ."

Juliette quickly protested. "No, no! Phillip, to say I am honored to be here with you and to hear all of this, is an understatement. I am realizing what you are sharing with me is something most people in the world will want—and need—to hear. Already, it is a message of hope and encouragement for *me*, and I didn't realize how much I needed it. Please, please, do continue."

Phillip smiled and nodded in appreciation of her words, and then he swiftly regained his place in the story . . .

"I was in awe. 'Patrick, it must have been amazing to be part of such an inspirational group of friends.'

"Patrick smiled. 'Well, it's kind of funny,' he said. 'I never saw myself as a person who could deeply impact people's lives. But being around these great souls gave me a belief in myself and brought out an encouraging mindset I didn't know I had. It did the same for each of us. Our various weaknesses—or difficulties—led to our ultimate strengths, and those strengths just happened to be ones that humankind needed.'

"I thought for a moment and pushed back from the table a bit, noticing our plates were clean. 'When did the group grow apart? I mean, it sounds like you all were destined to collaborate forever. When did everyone leave Dublin?'

"Patrick leaned back as if deep in thought. 'A few years ago. There were other exciting ventures after we wrote the books, but I would need much more time to share those stories with you. Those subsequent ventures were extremely intense and taxing on us all, so we eventually decided it was a younger man's—and woman's—game, and after many years, we were ready for simpler times. Each of us decided to go back to our home country and continue our lives of service from there. We still stay in touch, of course.' Patrick smiled.

"'How did you end up in New York?' I asked him.

"He chose his words carefully. 'I'm just here temporarily. New York was a special assignment for me.'

"I looked at Patrick like he was crazy. 'A special assignment? You mean . . . like, I was your assignment?'

"Patrick grinned. 'Okay, *assignment* is a little clinical. How about "project"?'

"'Project? That's even worse,' I said with a laugh.

"'Okay, how about . . . *opportunity*?'

"I grinned. 'Deal. I can live with being someone's opportunity. But who sent you on this trip to seek out your opportunity? And how did you know where to find me?'

"Patrick smiled and put up his hand. 'Wait, wait, you're asking too many questions. In fact, you haven't even begun your journey. How in the world do you expect me to answer all your questions when you don't yet know the right questions to ask . . . Mr. Opportunity?'

"Patrick's Irish laughter filled the room, and I couldn't help but laugh with him. But then, almost as quickly as it started, Patrick's laughter became muted and his voice softened as he said, 'Phillip, it seems you have agreed to travel to meet these powerful mentors. When will you be ready to leave? I'll need to get in touch with them to let them know you are coming.'

"I quickly replied, 'How about tomorrow? I have nothing tying me down here in New York. In fact, I'm ready to get out of here for a while. Where should I go first?'

"Patrick responded without hesitation. 'Your first stop should be Mexico to meet José Gonzales . . .'"

CHAPTER 6

The train was speeding toward its destination, and Juliette was still mesmerized by the story she was hearing.

Phillip continued, "After a good night's rest, I awoke the next morning excited about the upcoming days. I love traveling to exotic places—plus I always enjoy having conversations with wise people. This tour seemed as if it would check both of those boxes. Plus, the unshakable sadness that had overtaken my life made me desperate for *anything* that might help me find a degree of happiness again.

"After showering and eating a bite of breakfast, I packed quickly in anticipation of the adventure ahead. Then, jumping into my car and heading east on the short drive to the airport, I was still aware of my mind going a hundred miles an hour. *What would José be like? Where would he live? What stories would he have to share with me?*

"Once I arrived at the airport, the security line moved quickly, and I had a few minutes at the gate to think about what was waiting for me in Mexico.

Unfortunately, I had a few minutes to dwell on what was *behind* me—which I did far too often . . .

"I thought regularly about the great times my wife and I had in the early part of our relationship, but then those memories always devolved into ones of anger, grief, and disappointment. These were feelings I couldn't shake—no matter how much money I had. In fact, I found myself feeling more and more as if these traits were a permanent part of who I had become. Before the divorce, people referred to me as 'that happy guy who never gets upset about anything.' Now, behind my back, I wondered how they referred to me—maybe as 'the rich guy with a chip on his shoulder.'

"Right then, however, my thoughts were interrupted as a voice over the intercom blared, 'Now boarding for Cancún, flight 207.' I sprung out of my seat and headed toward the check-in. Within minutes I was, incredibly, on a plane taxiing out of New York City, headed to Mexico.

"It was a quick flight, and upon arrival at the Cancún airport, I pulled my suitcase off the conveyer belt in the baggage claim area and started scanning the crowd to find the driver Patrick said would meet me— Miguel was his name. Sure enough, as I began wading through what seemed like millions of people, I saw a gentleman who looked to be in his seventies, holding a sign that read PHILLIP WESTFORD.

"I made my way over to the man, who was about five and a half feet tall, stocky, with a mustache and a head full of dark, slicked-back hair. He was dressed neatly, with tropical-style light blue shorts and a pressed, untucked, white short-sleeved shirt. 'You must be Miguel,' I said with a big smile.

"He beamed, and with a crisp Spanish accent, replied, 'Yes señor, that's me!' Gesturing to an area ahead, he added, 'Our vehicle is just over there.'

"As I nodded, Miguel grabbed my luggage, and we walked the fifty yards or so to the parking lot, where he carefully placed the suitcase in the car's neatly organized trunk. I hopped in the passenger side, and as Miguel got in and gave a group of three employees at the airport a quick wave, we took off down the road, headed south.

"'We'll go for about an hour on the highway, and then we'll turn west into the jungle—the roads there aren't that great, but they're probably like some of the roads in the Missouri farmland,' he said with a smile, clearly pleased to tease his new passenger.

"I looked at Miguel in surprise. 'So, are you a mind reader, or did someone tell you I was from Missouri?'

"Miguel laughed. 'No, I wish I were a mind reader—it would help my marriage! Patrick told me a little about you yesterday.'

"'Ah, makes sense now. Do you talk with Patrick often?' I asked.

"He shrugged. 'Not as much as I would like. He is a fascinating man, but he doesn't call unless he's got someone he wants José to spend time with. I think the last person he sent here was a year and a half ago—that was Hilton.'

"'Hilton?'

"'Oh yes, sorry. Hilton Buckmeyer,' Miguel replied matter-of-factly.

"My look changed quickly to one of disbelief. 'Wait, you mean Hilton Buckmeyer, the English industrialist?'

"Miguel laughed. 'That's the one.'

"'Wow, José must have some special words of wisdom. Hilton Buckmeyer is one of the most successful men on the planet,' I added.

"Miguel shrugged again. 'I suppose. But then again, everyone that comes here is successful in some way. Hilton is also one of the *kindest* men on the planet. At least, he is now . . .'

"'What do you mean?'

"'Well, Hilton had a little bit of an arrogance problem when he arrived here,' Miguel said with a chuckle. 'But after a day or two with José, he was a new man. A much better man, in my humble opinion.' Before I could inquire further, Miguel exclaimed, 'Ah, I almost missed my turn! Let's take this little road into the jungle and see ol' José. Shouldn't be too much longer from here—sit back and enjoy the scenery.' With that, Miguel let down the window on my side, and the warm, tropical air filled the car.

"'Wow, there's no shortage of heat down here, is there? Then again, it beats being in Manhattan this chilly time of year.' I laughed.

"Miguel nodded and smiled. 'Yes, this is nice. The weather here is pleasant most of the time, although it does get a little, er, warm in the summer.'

"I laughed. 'Yeah, I bet.'

"We talked for another thirty minutes, and then Miguel slowed down to make a right turn onto a narrow, unmarked dirt road. He drove a few hundred more yards, and there on the left was a small home, beautifully framed with bamboo from top to bottom. The dwelling couldn't have been more than a thousand square feet, but the yard was beautifully landscaped with a wide variety of tropical plants and perfectly manicured, bright green grass. The entire property was lined with magnificent palm trees.

"Miguel stopped the car and looked at me with a grin. 'Not bad, huh?'

"Shaking my head and smiling, I replied, 'Everything seems so . . . perfect.'

"Miguel nodded. 'José is one of my favorite people to drive for. I have about fifty different business leaders and entrepreneurs who are clients, but José . . . he is special. The way he takes care of this property is the way he lives his whole life—simply and impeccably.'

"'Interesting,' I said with a nod. 'Sounds like José has got it all together. I could use some of that!'

"Miguel grinned. 'Well, I'm not sure José would say he's got it all together, but I think you'll find he can share some ideas with you that have dramatically improved his life, and maybe they can do the same for you.'

"As we stepped out of the car, the front door to the little cottage swung open, and a strong-looking man of medium height with shoulder-length dark hair and a thick mustache stepped out onto the front porch. He looked not much older than me.

"'Hola, friends!' he shouted with a big smile.

"I frowned. 'I'm afraid my Spanish is pretty weak.' I stuck out my hand and flashed a big grin. 'But I'm glad to meet you. I'm Phillip Westford.'

"At that moment, Miguel jumped into the conversation and said with a smile, 'Excuse me, José, but I must go. Lots of fares today—and that's a good thing.' He pointed to my suitcase which he had already taken out of the car and placed on the front porch, unbeknownst to me.

"'You're all set, amigo,' Miguel cheerfully said to me.

"I reached into my pocket to pay Miguel, but he put up his hand, shook his head, and smiled. 'No, no, José has already taken care of that. Enjoy your time in paradise!'

"José grinned and waved goodbye to Miguel before walking with me inside. As soon as we entered, a young golden retriever jumped playfully at me. 'Down, Rico!' José yelled with a laugh. Then turning to me, he continued his contagious chuckling and offered, 'Rico's only a puppy, but he can get scrappy. Hope you like dogs!'

"I looked at the beautiful pup and reached down to pet him as I said, 'Absolutely. I've had dogs all my life, until recently. Living in an apartment in the city just doesn't seem to work for me with pets.' I grinned. 'Someday I'll get another one.'

"José nodded kindly, and then stood up and went to the refrigerator, grabbing two bottles of cold water. As he handed one of them to me, he said, 'I'm glad you're here, Phillip. Patrick says we may have a lot to talk about.'

"I nodded in agreement, opened the bottle, and took a big gulp of the water. 'I'm still not sure how Patrick convinced me to come to Mexico, but . . .'

"José shook his head and wagged a finger at me, interjecting, 'I don't think he convinced you. When people come here, it's typically because they have convinced *themselves*. Patrick just has a knack for showing up to give folks a little nudge. Every time visitors come here, they are each a bit unsure, but then they leave saying the timing was perfect for them. Now, tell me about yourself. Why are you *really* here, Phillip?'

"'Why am I *really* here?' I wondered aloud. 'That's a good question.'

"'Excellent,' José responded jovially. 'What's the good answer?'

"Pondering, I leaned back and took another sip of water. 'Well, I suppose Patrick told you I won the lottery in the United States.'

"'Yes, he did. Congratulations . . . I guess.' José grinned.

"'You *guess*? What do you mean?' I responded with a puzzled look.

"'Well, surely everyone who wins the lottery is happier than they were before, right?' he asked with a wink.

"'Well, to tell you the truth . . . no. At least not me,' I offered sheepishly. 'In fact, the lottery has made my life much less happy. Sure, I have more *stuff*, and I can pretty much come and go as I please, but I don't know . . . something is missing. In fact, my life is just kind of a mess.'

"José rubbed his stubbled chin. 'I understand.'

"I was confused. 'You do? Have you been in a situation like mine?'

"José shrugged. 'I guess you could say that.'

"My perplexed look apparently urged José to continue. He leaned back and looked up as if trying to decide where to begin his story . . .

"'Although I was born here in Mexico, I grew up in a small town just south of Santiago, Chile. It's beautiful, the climate is mild, the people are friendly—it's like heaven on earth. I was a wild kid, and I never really cared about anything but having a good time and living a carefree life. Other people's problems were just that—*their* problems, not mine. If I was doing something that made me feel good, I was happy, and that's the way I planned on living the rest of my life.'

"I sat quietly, listening carefully as José continued, 'But my parents had other plans for me. Since I was not a particularly good student, they told me I had to do something constructive with my life after high school. So, once I graduated, I decided to join the Chilean army. It was the worst thing I ever did—and it also turned out to be the *best* thing I ever did.'

"I raised an eyebrow as José paused briefly, steepled his fingertips, then carried on . . .

"'Our unit was working in alliance with the British forces, fighting against the communists just outside of Lagos, Nigeria. All was going well, despite the horrible guerilla tactics the Nigerians used. Their forces were brutal to say the least. One day we were on a reconnaissance tour in the African desert . . .' José paused again and closed his eyes tightly. 'It happened so quickly. There was a flash, and then came the loudest explosion I had ever heard. Our lead person from England had stepped on a land mine. He and two other soldiers—one French and one Chilean like me—were killed instantly. It's the last memory I have of the battlefield.'

"I sat entranced as José carried on.

"'I woke up the next day in a makeshift military hospital ten miles from Lagos. I could barely hear, I had horrible wounds from the shrapnel, and my head was wrapped with a bloody bandage. As I slowly regained consciousness, I saw there was a gentleman with an Irish accent sitting in a chair next to my bed, kindly holding my hand and offering a soft prayer for me. It turns out the man was a chaplain for the Irish unit. Seeing him, I assumed I was about to die, and he was there to give me the last rites. I was only eighteen years old, and until that point I had never considered I might not survive the war. But the chaplain gave me a glimmer of hope as he looked at me and confidently said, "Young man, we are going to get you better and get you home." Those simple words gave me so much encouragement and relief, I just started sobbing. He gently touched my head and said another short prayer over me. Strangely enough, at that moment I felt something inside me change, as if this man had miraculous powers. However, he insisted it was simply God working through him, and I fully believed him. I stopped crying, and I somehow knew that everything was going to be okay. Don't ask me how, because I was in horrible shape, but I knew I would heal and get home, just like the chaplain had said.'

"I looked at José in disbelief. 'I don't suppose I have ever talked with someone who has been through something like that. What happened next?'

"José smiled softly. 'They moved me to a highly specialized military hospital, and I began the work of getting back to normal. Every day I went through therapy—both mental and physical therapy. Plus,' José said with a smile, 'every day, that same chaplain would come by and visit me—just to check in.'

"'Like a guardian angel, huh?' I found myself saying.

"José nodded and smiled. 'Exactly. I looked forward to those visits so much. The chaplain became my good friend. He was so wise that I couldn't get enough of our conversations. Every day I soaked up his words and his encouragement. I came to find that his name . . . was Patrick O'Rourke.

"'That's right, Phillip,' José said with a smile when he saw the astonished look on my face.

"Jose' went on, 'Finally, the day came when I was ready to be discharged. I knew I was a different person. The war had changed me, but thankfully, Patrick had changed me even more. His philosophy was one that I wanted to have as well. He taught me what was important in life are the people, the experiences, the acts of love—and the ability to help others on their journeys. The fact that Patrick always seemed to be there for me and have my best interest in mind was inspiring and different from the way I had lived my life. I had always been a reckless, even selfish young man, but that all changed after that fateful day in the desert and the subsequent words and deeds of generosity from

Patrick. You could say that experience made me the man I am today—and I am deeply grateful.'

"José continued, 'Finally, as I walked to the front of the hospital the day I was to be released, there were probably fifty staff members and patients there to cheer for me. I still remember the applause as I walked down the hall. Then as I reached the front door, there was Patrick—cheering like crazy. He had this huge smile, and as I walked by, he looked at me, leaned in, and whispered, "I told you we were going to get you healed and get you home. Now, that time has come." I waved goodbye to the other patients and to that amazing medical team and thanked each of them for what they had done for me. Then I looked at Patrick and told him there was no way for me to describe how appreciative I was for his help, and I would never forget his heartfelt words of support. He smiled and said, "My friend, the best days are ahead—I will see you soon." I didn't know exactly what he meant by that, but I mentally tucked those words away. I returned home to Chile to a hero's welcome, and it was . . . indescribable. Seeing my parents so proud of me and knowing that I was a new person in so many ways was gratifying. But the most gratifying thing was what happened years later. I was living a quiet life in Santiago, and one day when I went to the mailbox, there was a letter from overseas addressed to me. I looked at the return address and it immediately brought tears to my eyes . . .

"'The letter was from Patrick O'Rourke.'"

CHAPTER 7

At that moment, the train began slowing down, and then it came to a complete stop. As the train's whistle sounded, the shout of, "Newbridge for thirty minutes!" echoed through the cabins.

Juliette looked at Phillip, and he seemed to know what she was thinking. "Yes, time is flying, isn't it? We are already halfway to Cork," he said. "In fact, I wish we had more than a half hour here—Newbridge has apparently got quite a bit of history."

"Maybe on my next trip. I'm more interested in staying on the train and hearing where your story goes . . ." As Phillip nodded, Juliette added, "What you are sharing with me is mind-boggling. I feel like I know these people—the images are so vivid."

Phillip grinned. "I'll always remember each person on that journey. They provided me with lessons I needed at just the right time . . ."

Juliette responded wistfully, "I can see I need these same lessons. I have often wondered what 'lessons' I am being taught since everything that happened in New

York. Journalism is my calling, and I was always sure I was in the right place there, but now . . ."

"I'm thinking . . . you are *exactly* where you need to be," Phillip interjected softly.

"I hope so," she said with a sigh and a look of uncertainty. "I really hope so . . ."

Phillip continued his intriguing story.

"José said when he pulled that letter from the mailbox, he began reading slowly, as if to savor every word from his mentor. It read:

Dear José,

What a gift it was to meet you those years ago in Nigeria—I feel certain that God brought us together.

I believed from the moment I met you after the explosion that you were destined for greatness. Now that we have spent this time together, I am sure of it. You have gifts that will benefit many people.

I am no longer a chaplain, but I am now part of a small firm in Dublin that specializes in making people's lives happier. It may sound vague, but trust me, what I do is exactly what I was meant to do, and it is what I believe you were also meant to do.

I would like to make a proposal to you: come to Ireland and let me teach you the skills we use at the firm to better the lives of others. If you accept, I am willing to pay you handsomely. Let's just say you will not have to worry about money for quite some time.

Enclosed is a check for two thousand pounds which will more than cover your travel expenses if you choose to join our team. If you decide not to, please do with the money as you wish. I trust your judgment will be excellent, so I have no concerns about how it will be spent.

Your friend,

Patrick

Juliette was spellbound as Phillip's narrative continued.

"José looked at me as if he was reliving an experience that had just happened, although it had been many years ago. He then said in a voice full of confidence, 'I trusted Patrick, I loved adventures, and with my newfound philosophy of living, I couldn't see how this opportunity could be anything but a win-win. Even though I had no idea what this new job entailed, I bought a one-way ticket from Santiago to Dublin, and I was on my way two days later.' José continued, 'When I reached Dublin, I looked up Patrick's address and took the first cab to his residence. You have seen it before, haven't you, Phillip?' he asked me.

"I shook my head. 'I've only seen his place in Manhattan.'

"'Well, it's quite beautiful. Anyway, Patrick greeted me at his home with a massive bear hug. It was as if I were a long-lost son. Making a sweeping gesture, he said, "José, welcome to my humble abode. And welcome to a new life, one you will never regret embarking upon. I assure you it was a wise choice.'" José smiled at the memory and said, 'It turned out that Patrick, Ahmet, and David had become internationally-renowned inspirational writers, and Patrick had developed a new business with the two men—one which would now include me. Patrick saw how evil, fascism, and communism had gotten such a stronghold in so many countries, and he wanted to do what he could to ensure the world was a safer, better place for all and for future generations. Our little company used the same ideas that Patrick, David, and Ahmet used in their influential, powerful writings. The mission was to go to countries and train the heads of state to make a positive difference by teaching them lessons on courage, faith, strength, and compassion. Leaders were standing in line to have our group work with them—especially after their first client.'

"My puzzled look made José grin as he added, 'They called him the President of the United States of America.'

"I was speechless. 'Wait. What? The President was a client?'

"José nodded and chuckled. 'Yes, that was before my time with the firm, but I know they didn't want to mess that one up.'

"I still couldn't quite grasp the magnitude of it all, and José saw my look of confusion, so he elaborated. 'It turns out the President was a huge fan of their writings, and when he found out the men were starting a leadership consulting group, he contacted Patrick and signed on immediately. Needless to say, our business took off after that.'

"I interjected, 'So, this was mostly attitude and personal growth work, I guess?'

"José shook his head. 'Much more than that. It was a method we developed to powerfully and permanently change leaders from the inside out—turning them into unshakeable spiritual warriors, if you will. We worked with kings and queens, princes and princesses, and many other presidents. It was all done under the radar. Almost no one knew when we were in a country—or knew when we were gone—but what we left behind were rulers that were prepared to change the planet wisely, ethically, and courageously. Every leader that went through the program admitted that Patrick and our team were unlike any consultants they had ever had in their countries. When we departed, the leaders were new people—and I daresay the world was a safer place.'

"I paused and then found myself saying, 'Almost like worldwide guardian angels.'

"José smiled. 'I see your intuitive senses are becoming heightened. The name of the company was GGA Incorporated. Global Guardian Angels . . .'

"I shook my head in wonder. It was all starting to make sense now, the concept of strengthening others by transforming our own painful lessons into fully authentic power.

"José's deep voice pierced the silence that had filled the room. 'I thought back to the time I was in that hospital in the desert. I remembered how Patrick simply touched me on the forehead, and I felt his love and kindness. It was an almost mystical presence I knew I would never forget.'

"At that point, José stopped his story, looked at me, and said, 'Phillip, here is a great piece of the puzzle to understanding what we did, which I sense you are already starting to grasp: each of us used the tragedies we had been through and turned them into something that would benefit the world. There was no other way to get the wisdom or the strength we needed to help others—but to transcend these challenges ourselves. It is the same for you, my friend.'

"I couldn't believe what I was hearing, Juliette— these words seemed custom-designed for me.

"José saw the look on my face and grinned. 'It's really that simple, Phillip—but it is not *easy*. All of us go through tremendous difficulties and pain. But most people spend their lives with guilt or regret, wishing things had gone differently for them—yet never doing anything with that suffering. Of course, I know there are times we must feel deep sadness—that is human nature. But those who can take their agony and convert it to make others' lives better will find their own lives altered in a magnificent way. Do you understand, Phillip?'

"'Yes, I think I do,' I said with a fervent nod, urging him to continue.

"'When you have been through a tragedy,' José told me, 'and you have this deep desire to transform the pain to help others, it *will* gradually change you—and then it becomes part of your presence, which will allow you to positively influence others. It is what Patrick, Ahmet, David, and I understood, and the concept is supremely powerful for the giver and the receiver.'

"Shaking my head in disbelief at what I was hearing, I asked, 'So, José, how many international leaders did the team work with over the years?'

"José shrugged. 'Maybe one hundred.'

"I was astonished. 'One hundred? So, by working with that many leaders, who in turn influenced millions of their people, your small group basically *shaped the world!*'

"José smiled and nodded appreciatively. 'We stayed together for many years. But at some point, we decided to start using our talents in ways that would affect individuals like yourself. We found the global leaders were diligent about using what we taught them, but the travel and the intensity of the work got to be too much for us. We were proud of what we had done, and we felt the timing was good for us to exit. Gratefully, there are new companies that have come up to fill our shoes—but like we were, they are essentially invisible.'

"'Now,' José said, 'it's a slower pace, but the lessons we teach are still the same. When one of us discovers a worthy candidate, we let others in the group know, and we set up the training. Knowing each other as we do, we can be assured the candidates we find will maintain the integrity of our teachings and wield their new skills wisely.'

"'How do you find candidates?' I wondered aloud.

"José smiled and pointed at me. 'How did Patrick find *you*?'

"I muttered, 'Well, I thought I found Patrick. I saw him sitting on a bench one day in New York, and I just sensed he had something I needed . . .'

"José held up his hand to interrupt me gently. '*Precisely*, my friend. When one develops into a person who embodies the strong, positive spiritual traits we teach, others recognize it, and the right people are drawn to you. Patrick knew you were in Manhattan, and he not only knew you needed help, but he also believed from everything he had heard that you had "been through the fire of life" and had the potential to impact many others. He trusted you would be put in his path at the right time. That is what the Bible refers to as "faith that can move mountains," Phillip. Of course,' José said with a wink, 'he knew you'd need a little bit of training, which is where your new friends, Ahmet, David, and myself, will help.'

"At his words, I felt chills as I thought to myself, *In a way, Patrick really was my guardian angel . . .*

"I shook my head and quietly said, 'It's just miraculous!'

"José quickly replied, 'Yes, you could certainly see it that way. We are all capable of having the type of faith that creates miracles.'

"I was taking it all in and had so many more questions to ask, but Rico jumped playfully into José's lap and broke up the depth of conversation. With great care, José caught the dog and pulled him closer, laughing. 'Too bad people can't all be like dogs, wouldn't you say, Phillip? Fun, easygoing, trusting, not caught up in ego. Ah, yes, it would be so much better.'

"I grinned and agreed. 'No doubt about it, José. By the way, how did you end up in Mexico?'

"He nodded in affirmation of the question and answered, 'I love it here—always have. As I mentioned, this is where I was born, and later I was one of the consultants who came to Mexico to work with its leaders, and I knew I would settle here someday. I love the people, the land, the weather—and it is not too far from Santiago in the big scheme of things. Plus, the jungle here is so peaceful.'

"I grinned. 'It's sure better than New York.'

"'Well,' he said, 'there definitely aren't as many snowstorms.'

"We both laughed, and then José became more serious. 'Phillip, I know what you went through with your family, and I know how you have suffered. I want you to understand this: happiness is always yours for the taking. You can spend your days being bitter and resentful, or you can spend them being grateful for all the good you have and for the opportunities that lie before you. Patrick helped me believe I could make that same choice when I was lying in the hospital bed in Nigeria. I decided life was too short, and there were so many people who could use my help and benefit from my experience.' Then, José paused and thoughtfully commented, 'From this short time I have spent with you, I understand why Patrick sent you here.'

"'Really?' I asked. 'Why do you say that?'

"'Because he saw you have down deep what we all have—courage, faith, and strength. But there is something else about you. You have great compassion for people and for all living things, and I believe that you have a unique ability to make a difference in the world. But it is time for you to *choose* to use those God-given gifts and channel your bitterness, anger, and resentment into something that can make others' lives better. The choice is yours—and no one can take that away from you.'

"I looked at him and smiled. Something about his words resonated with me as I sat in the Mexican jungle that day. Maybe I *did* have it in me, and now I was starting to understand what possibilities were available to me—and to others whose lives I could make a difference in. The wonderful part was . . . it had nothing to do with my wealth.

"José looked at me with a grin as if he knew how excited I was to begin grasping these truths. 'Now, my good man, we have sat here for hours. I have some things I must do—and Rico would like to take his daily exercise. Will you join us for a walk and then stay the night?'

"'It would be a privilege,' I replied warmly.

"We talked as we walked Rico, and then we talked more over dinner that evening. José shared inspirational stories from his years with the Chilean army and of his times traveling the globe. His words were not only wise, but riveting. He was a careful listener also. I talked with him about the struggles I had endured with the lottery winnings' effect on my life and thanked him for his encouraging advice to help me through my current situation.

"We ended the night by a firepit José had prepared behind his home. As if he wanted to give me time to digest what I had heard, we simply sat in contemplation, exchanging only a few words as we enjoyed the sounds of the jungle and the peacefulness all around. I savored the feelings that came over me—feelings of healing and gratitude for what I had learned from this wise man.

"When the roaring fire finally faded, José and I realized we were fading also, and so we put out the remaining cinders and headed inside for a much-needed night of rest.

"After eight glorious hours of sleep, I awoke to the smell of a wonderful Mexican breakfast José had prepared. As I headed down the hall toward the kitchen, I heard José's booming voice calling to me: 'I want to make sure you don't leave hungry as you start another day of travel. If I am not mistaken, it is time for you to go see someone else—Ahmet Mansour. You will find him one of the most fascinating people you have ever met.'

"'Really? He's that special?' I cocked my head, and he quickly acknowledged the display of curiosity.

"'Yes, but it will be quite the journey. He is far outside Cairo. In fact, he is probably one hundred miles into the desert. You thought the Mexican jungle was remote? Well, wait until you see his place in El Sadir!'

"'I can't wait,' I said with a smile as we sat down and began devouring the delicious meal. Afterward, I got my belongings together and came back to the den where José was now sitting. 'Thank you so much, my friend. My eyes have already been opened to the opportunities out there for me. I am starting to see what a difference I can make—but I feel there are more pieces of the puzzle I need to put together.'

"José nodded. 'You are spot-on, Phillip. I bet this next stop will help put some of those pieces in place.'

José motioned to the door. 'Come on, I'll walk you out to the driveway. Miguel should be here by now to take you to the airport.'

"As we walked out front, there was Miguel, leaning up against the car, looking toward us and petting an obviously receptive Rico.

"'He came running out the door like he had been waiting for me for hours—what did you do, scare the poor dog, José?' Miguel grinned.

"'Yes, I think he was terrified he was going to have to listen to me pontificate, so he darted out of the house when he got the chance.'

"The three of us laughed as Miguel opened the door for me to get in on the passenger side. Letting down the window, I stuck out my hand to José one last time. 'José, it was a pleasure to meet you and spend time with you. I hope our paths cross again in the future.'

"He nodded and smiled. 'Well, you know where I live now, and I am not going anywhere. You're welcome any time—that is, if you can handle the heat and the hyper dog!'

"I smiled, and Miguel slowly began backing the car out of the driveway. We both waved to José, and then we were quickly out on the jungle road.

"I shook my head and looked at Miguel. '*Wow* is all I can say.'

"'I told you!' Miguel shot back as he playfully hit my shoulder. 'He has such wisdom, but he also has such kindness and humility.'

"I sat expressionless, shaking my head in awe.

"Miguel paused and then glanced at me as the car headed down the small road. 'Well, then again, your time with Ahmet in Egypt is also going to be unforgettable. That man's story— it is incredible, as you'll hear.' I looked over at Miguel and saw he was nodding in admiration as he thought about Ahmet.

"The drive to the airport seemed short, probably because my head was still spinning from the insights José had shared with me in his secluded, beautiful little place in the jungle. Regardless of the reason, it was now time to get out of the car, as Miguel pulled into a convenient parking spot.

"'Egyptair, Phillip. That's you,' Miguel offered with a smile.

"I stepped out of the cab and looked up at the EGYPTAIR sign, then looked back at Miguel.

"'Yep, as crazy as it seems, I guess you're right—I'm headed to the Middle East.' I walked around the cab, shook Miguel's hand, and thanked him profusely. I also started to reach into my pocket for some cash.

"'Nope,' he smiled. 'You know the drill by now— it's taken care of. Now, safe travels, my friend—learn lots in Egypt.'

"I smiled and nodded, wondering to myself how I could possibly learn more . . ."

CHAPTER 8

Juliette gazed out the window as the train continued its journey, now well into the breathtaking scenery of southern Ireland. Phillip leaned back in his seat and breathed deeply, taking a break from his story.

Juliette spoke up. "It seems unimaginable to meet a person like that, Phillip. Especially in a place like the Mexican jungle . . ."

Phillip shook his head. "Yes, I was thinking how surreal the whole experience was. I mean, just a day before I was in Manhattan talking with a crazy old man in the park—well, I *thought* he was crazy—and then twenty-four hours later, I was in southern Mexico talking to a guru in the jungle and loving every minute of it." He smiled.

Juliette rubbed her chin thoughtfully and said, "You know, this is such a great example of the adage 'teachers are everywhere.' Or maybe I should say, the *classroom* is everywhere. I think about people like my dad and even David Marlow, and I realize they had lessons to teach me, although they were seldom pleasant. They had their own type of stories I needed—stories that have led me to where I am today, just as you suggested earlier."

Phillip nodded. "The older I get, the more I realize how true that is."

Juliette smiled. "I guess it kind of makes it all more bearable when you can look back and see how the pieces fit together. Plus, it gives a person confidence that what happens to us in the future will also be synchronistic, if we choose to see it that way."

"Well," Phillip interjected, "it may seem like splitting hairs, but the situations *are* all synchronistic, even if we don't want to see them that way. I think that is part of maturing on our spiritual journeys: understanding the value and importance in each interaction, whether we 'like' the interactions, or not."

Juliette smiled and nodded as she took in her new mentor's words. She was eager for more as she blurted out, "So, then what happened, Phillip? Did you really go to Egypt?"

"Oh, yes. Egypt was like no place I have ever been, and Ahmet Mansour was like no person I've ever met."

Ready to be immersed in the story again, Juliette nodded encouragingly as Phillip carried on . . .

"It was a fourteen-hour flight from Cancún to Cairo, and fortunately I slept most of the way. I didn't realize how tired I still was. When the flight arrived in Egypt, just like in Mexico, it was almost unbearably hot. Also, like at the airport in Cancún, the Cairo

Airport was insanely crowded. I could barely move without bumping into someone.

"Suddenly I heard a voice calling my name, and I turned in all directions to see who it was. Just about twenty feet away in the sea of people, to my right, I spotted him desperately trying to speak over the crowd. 'Mr. Westford! I am your driver, Karim Abdallah! Come around the side, and I will meet you by the white car near the airport sign.'

"I started walking in that direction and eventually pushed my way through all the people to stand face-to-face with Karim. He was a sophisticated-looking Egyptian gentleman of average height, with round, wire-framed glasses, and he had a slightly balding head of black hair. Honestly, he looked more like a doctor than a cab driver. Turned out he truly *was* a doctor . . .

"Smiling, I reached out my hand to greet him and asked, 'How did you know who I was?' The man laughed, and shaking my outstretched hand, replied, 'Look around! You are the only non-Egyptian person coming off this flight, starting with your blonde hair . . .'

"I couldn't help but chuckle as I looked all about and saw he was correct. 'Okay, you've got a good point there. Where to, my friend?'

"He turned and gestured toward the east. 'We're headed to the Sahara Desert. Hope you've ridden a camel before,' he said with a grin.

"The look on my face showed I had definitely *not* ridden an animal like that recently, or ever.

"Karim threw his head back and cackled in delight. 'Just kidding. No camels involved on this trip—although it is about two hours to get to Ahmet's home, and there is quite a bit of desert involved.'

"I breathed a sigh of relief that I'm sure was obvious. 'Well, I'm glad to hear about the camels, and I'll see how the desert goes for me. There's not a lot of that back in Manhattan, but I've always been good at acclimating to my surroundings.' I grinned.

"'Great, then let's go,' he said. He placed my luggage in the trunk of his small, black car, walked around to start it, and I jumped in the passenger's seat as the engine rumbled to life."

Phillip stopped, looked at Juliette, and said with a look of wonder, "As we left the airport and headed into the desert, I had never seen so much sand in my life! As we drove south past the Sphynx, I was overwhelmed by how different the country was from America—it was just like the pictures in my history books as a youth. It was magnificent."

Juliette smiled. "I can only imagine. Not like Des Moines at all."

Phillip chuckled and continued.

"Driving along, we had some fascinating conversations. It turned out Karim and Ahmet had met three years before and became best of friends. Karim recounted how he and Ahmet were both members of a distinctive club in Cairo.

"'It isn't a club of wealth or status, but of simplicity,' Karim said with a smile.

"I looked at him with obvious confusion.

"Karim explained, 'It is a group of about fifty people dedicated to a lifestyle of uncomplicatedness. We don't need to buy expensive items or fancy homes because we have each learned that the keys to a happier life don't cost anything at all: peace, joy, love, and kindness are our focus. Even though we are all financially comfortable, we know from our own experiences that it's the *intangibles* in our lives that cannot be taken away. People come from around the world to visit our little group, and they often take our ideas back home and become much happier people as a result. I can't tell you the number of correspondences I have received over the years from visitors thanking us for what they learned during their time with us.'

"I leaned back and nodded my approval. 'What a terrific idea, Karim. It's interesting how so few folks in the world—maybe especially in the USA—don't understand that concept. Sadly, it's a mentality that has not been a part of my own life in a long, long time.'

"'Well,' Karim replied, 'the job of a good marketing company is to keep that message of simplicity from getting through to people. Instead, they want folks to believe they *need* to have the products the company is selling, to be happy. When you pound that theme into peoples' heads through billboards and commercials and magazines, well, they start to believe it.'

"'Makes sense to me,' I replied. 'The more I think about it, I have found myself falling victim to that kind of nonsense again and again. It's like we must constantly be on guard to fend off and filter out the crazy, almost hypnotic messages.'

"Karim nodded in agreement, then asked, 'So, what brings you to see Ahmet?'

"'Um, well, I guess you could say a friend referred me,' I sheepishly replied.

"'Ah, so Patrick sent you.' He winked.

"I laughed. 'So, you know Patrick, too! I seem to forget that Patrick is apparently popular around the world.'

"Karim nodded. 'Oh, there's no doubt about that. But I will also say that he is one of the humblest men you'll ever meet. Plus, if Patrick invited you to come here, you were a wise man to take him up on his offer. It means he saw tremendous potential in you. I think you'll find your time with Ahmet well worth the journey. By the way, how was your visit with José?'

"'Okay, so you also know José, huh? You guys are a tight group.' I laughed again.

"'The tightest!' he beamed. 'Yes, José is another remarkable person. I have only met him once, and

I will never forget it. His presence is impeccable and captivating.'

"'I certainly agree,' I replied. 'If Ahmet can teach me even half of what I learned from José, I'll be impressed,' I said with a chuckle.

"'You will not be disappointed, my friend.' Karim grinned.

"After we had driven for what seemed like hours through the sweltering desert, we reached a gorgeous home. Although it was not a large house, the beige stone facade was magnificent. There was also an inviting, completely landscaped pool area just visible around the right side of the home, and lush gardens with palm trees scattered across the property provided shade.

"As we stepped out of the car, even in the oppressive heat, there seemed to be an air of peace. Ahmet walked out to greet us, and I immediately felt comfortable with him. He was a large, muscular man with a full, black beard, and he had the appearance of a wrestler you would see on television. He looked at Karim, smiled broadly, then grabbed his hand and shook it fervently. 'How are you, my old friend?'

"'Great, Ahmet!' replied Karim with an equally big grin. 'Always good to see you, my brother.' Karim gestured kindly toward me. 'Ahmet, this is Phillip, our friend from the United States.'

"I reached out and shook his hand, which was so large it engulfed mine. 'Nice to meet you, Ahmet. I've heard lots about you.'

"Ahmet smiled, and with a twinkle in his eye, he replied, 'Well, don't believe any of it—especially if it came from Patrick O'Rourke.'

"'Ah, yes, that's exactly where I heard it!' We both laughed.

"Just then, Karim spoke up and said, 'Ahmet, I must get back on the road—I have a meeting in Cairo late this afternoon. Could I trouble you for a few bottles of water?'

"'It's a pleasure, my good fellow. I hear there's a big desert out there—a man could get thirsty!'

"Karim laughed and wiped the sweat from his brow. 'Sometimes I think you've got the right idea, staying out here away from the city. Maybe when I get older, I'll be a hermit like you.' He grinned.

"Ahmet handed him the water and replied, 'Hey, the hermit life isn't half bad after all those years I spent in Dublin. Don't knock it until you've tried it.' The two men laughed in unison.

"'Thanks for taking time out of your schedule to bring our new friend here,' Ahmet said appreciatively.

"'Any time.' Then using an Egyptian term of close friendship, he added, 'I'll see you soon, ya sahby.' With that, Karim hopped back in his vehicle and headed out into the desert, a trail of dust lagging behind the vehicle as he drove.

"'Come on in, Phillip,' Ahmet said as he gestured toward the inside of the home. 'Let's have a seat at the kitchen table. I've got some mint tea brewing, and I think you'll like it.'

"I nodded and followed him into the house, closing the large, solid wooden door behind me as I entered. Just like the homes of Patrick and José, the interior was flawless. Everything was in its place, and the sandstone flooring throughout the house was stunning.

"'How did you find such a beautiful home in the middle of the desert?' I asked.

"Ahmet shrugged and grinned. 'I built it.'

"'You built it . . . yourself? I can't believe it. Any kind of construction is not my talent, so I am doubly amazed.'

"'Well, thank you. It's just me living here, so it's kind of cozy, I guess you could say. I like it just fine.'

"I nodded in agreement. After we sat down at the kitchen table, the tea kettle whistled. 'Ah, just in time,' Ahmet said with a laugh. He jumped back up, grabbed two cups, and then pulled the kettle off the stove. 'Cream and sugar, Phillip?'

"'If that's the way you recommend it, that's perfect,' I said. 'By the way, thank you for sending Karim to pick me up.'

Ahmet smiled. '*Doctor Karim Abdallah* to be precise.'.'

"'Karim is a doctor?'

"'Yes, he is a brilliant surgeon. I assume he told you about our Simplicity Club.'

"'Yes, and I was fascinated,' I replied in earnest.

"Ahmet nodded. 'Well, he *is* a fascinating man. He became extraordinarily wealthy, but the money took over his life. He lost all perspective, and then one day he understood he was being seduced by the *things* and messages of the world. Up to that point, he didn't understand why he felt so unfulfilled—even though he had every good and service you can imagine. He was miserable.'

"I couldn't help but interject, 'Wow, his situation sounds just like mine . . .'

"Ahmet nodded. 'Karim was referred to our club by a mutual friend, and he fell in love with the concepts we espouse. When he and I first talked, we realized we had much in common from our journeys. We became friends almost instantly, and we have been ever since. Dr. Abdallah lives a simple life now, and he would tell you he has never been this happy.'

"I shook my head in awe. 'That's a powerful story, Ahmet.'

"'Yes, and it speaks to the power of developing solid, core beliefs which create a presence to attract like-minded people.'

"I nodded, realizing how much those words echoed the philosophy José had shared with me. Ahmet then brought the two cups of tea to the table, and I sipped mine as he did. It was a unique and flavorful brew. 'I've never had mint tea,' I said with a look of surprise. 'It's tasty!'

"Ahmet smiled and shrugged. 'Well, it seems all Egyptian food and drink has mint in it, so I keep a good bit on hand. I'm kind of partial to it, also.'

"I continued sipping the soothing, light green drink. Then Ahmet's tone became a bit more tempered as he said, 'You know, Phillip, I had a conversation with Patrick before you arrived, and he told me about your lottery experience and what happened with your family. So, where are you at this point in your life—as far as how you feel about yourself and others?'

"It was a question I wasn't ready for, and Ahmet saw the pensive look on my face.

"'No thinking, just be blunt with me,' he said with a smile.

"I decided to take his advice. 'I have felt bitter, angry, and disappointed for a long time, if you must know. I mean, the whole despicable lottery journey has sucked the life out of me. I've seen my relationships crumble, and I am constantly looking over my shoulder—often literally—wondering who is coming to try and take advantage of me. I've become sad and cynical, and lately, I have even felt like giving up on life.'

"Ahmet paused thoughtfully, then looked at me with deep compassion and replied in his baritone voice, 'I understand, my friend. When we feel betrayed, defeated, and alone, we can eventually become inconsolable. But in my opinion, it is fine to feel that way . . . for a while.'

"I guess he again saw my puzzled look, and he added, 'Here's what I mean: even though we often won't admit it, we *know* we have a choice every day as to whether or not we will accept what life brings us. We are going to get hurt, and we are going to feel bad sometimes—this is inevitable, even for the great spiritual masters. But at some point, if we don't take the pain, channel it, and then let go, it festers, and the only people who really suffer are . . . us. I know from experience this is true.'

"I listened carefully as he continued: 'Phillip, years ago, my days felt so long that I often did not want to get out of bed in the mornings. I was in my teenage years, depressed, and due to a horrible series of events, I was living on my own, simply trying to survive. I will tell you more about this later, but trust me, I understand the pain and sadness you are feeling.'

"'Thank you, Ahmet,' I said quietly. 'Somehow, I do feel you understand, and I am grateful for your empathetic words.'

"Maybe it was his compassion, or maybe it was his wise, gentle tone, but something about Ahmet reminded me of Patrick, which made me ask, 'Ahmet, how did you come to meet Mr. O'Rourke?'

"Ahmet smiled as if he had known that question was coming. 'Ah, yes, Patrick O'Rourke—one of the finest men I have ever had the pleasure of knowing.'

"'I'm definitely seeing a pattern,' I said with a laugh. 'Everyone I've asked says that same thing about him.'

"Ahmet nodded his agreement, then leaned back and looked up. 'I guess I was around twenty-five years old when I first met him. By that time, I had graduated from the University of Cairo, and I was teaching there. One summer I took a sabbatical and went to Ireland—Dublin specifically. I loved it so much that I decided to move there, and I was fortunate to get a job at the University of Dublin teaching psychology. I met Patrick in a therapy group we were both involved in. He was a broken man, as any of us would be in his situation, but I saw through that pain, and I knew from looking into his eyes that this man was special—we became instant friends. As you may know, Patrick later became a chaplain and began working to help others heal from their own traumas.'

"I nodded as I thought back on Patrick's words about those earlier times of grief. 'I know they were dark days for him.'

"'Yes, of course,' replied Ahmet. 'But Patrick would also tell you that what he went through was preparation for helping others in a way he could never have done without his suffering.'

"I shook my head. 'Pain is inevitable for all of us, isn't it?'

"'Exactly, Phillip. At some point, we all will deal with traumas and tragedies and deep pain. Life is a series of potential hurts, punctuated by times of happiness. If we wait for life to be "easy" or problem-free, we'll be waiting forever.'

"I jumped in. 'But, Ahmet, I *really* want to find peace in my life, and I just can't find it no matter where I look!'

"Then Ahmet looked into my eyes, and without flinching said, 'Phillip, you do not *look* for peace. You *choose* peace—at any time. It is always there, waiting for you.'

"His words had pierced my soul—but my ego did not want to believe it could be that simple. 'It sounds good, Ahmet, but when you are going through those difficult things, it's not so easy.'

"'Of course not!' Ahmet said, now excitedly throwing up his hands. 'That is why most people don't choose peace at those times. It is much easier to complain about our problems and hope that better days are ahead. Well, better days will *never* be ahead when we think like that, and the more we complain, the worse we feel. Phillip, although we will still feel pain, we must create those better days by fundamentally choosing to have a peaceful spirit, learning from our difficulties, then pressing on *in spite* of the heartache.'

"I nodded in understanding as Ahmet continued.

"'But, my friend, the final piece to all of that is using the lessons to empathize with and help others who haven't figured this out yet.'

"'So, how do we do *that*?' I asked curiously. 'I feel so overwhelmed by my own problems, I don't even know how to *start* helping others with theirs.'

"He smiled, shaking his head gently. 'The secret is often for us to help people by *doing* less for them.'

"'What? Do less? Just sit back and let them struggle?'

"'Maybe, but not in the way you might think,' he replied evenly. 'We can't rescue every person from their own problems . . . but we can often facilitate them rescuing themselves.'

"Now I was really confused. 'It sounds to me like you're saying we should not even *try* to help others.'

"Ahmet smiled, shook his head slowly, and said, 'Not at all. That is apathy. I am suggesting the opposite—empathy. It's one of the most powerful forces on earth, and it's available any time. We can use it to actively listen, care, and offer an authentic presence instead of telling others what to do or trying to solve their problems for them—because we don't always *know* the right thing to do! Not only that, if we spoon-feed answers, there is no growth through the situations. Phillip, there is often nothing more healing and empowering to someone who is going through difficulties than to have a friend sit with them and offer no solutions, but instead simply give love, peace, and understanding—without any judgments. That is what I mean by doing less.'

"I nodded tentatively. 'I understand. I can relate to that because when our lottery problems started, no matter what I said to her, my wife would not change, and she continued with her destructive behavior. So, you're saying giving advice doesn't usually help, huh?'

"'Well, there are times we know the correct answer, and we can offer that—but those are exceptional times. Plus, advice is often not what people want. In times of despair and struggle, they more often want to be heard, understood, and valued. If people are going to change, like your wife, for example, they must *want* to change. As I said, the best thing we can do, in my opinion, is to provide a safe, nurturing environment so transformation and growth can happen—*if* they're going to happen.'"

At that point, Phillip thoughtfully looked at Juliette and reflected, "I just sat there, quietly pondering Ahmet's words."

She replied, "I understand. I know I would have done the same thing. It's interesting to hear someone talk about simply being present and peaceful instead of trying to force some action or response. I tend to want to break the silence in the room and offer a solution to fix the problem. What Ahmet said fits in nicely with what my dad said about not forcing anything."

Phillip nodded. "Yes, it was eye-opening for me. I, too, realized how often I probably had tried to give advice in situations where advice wasn't really what the person wanted or needed. In fact, it really put me on a journey of *doing* less. Instead, I started to focus on *being*—being present, being genuine, being compassionate. I now see that is one of the most unselfish approaches we can take in dealing with problems—ours or those of others."

Juliette paused and then offered, "The challenge, as you suggested, is that people in our culture often equate that attitude with indifference or laziness—not 'doing' anything."

Phillip nodded. "Well, yes, I think that's true. But now I do see it's just the opposite. It's about being fully conscious, relaxed—and trusting the outcome as we discussed before. It's knowing the answer will come—if an answer is even needed. Again, it's a manifestation of our faith."

Juliette smiled. "That kind of attitude is something I can't be reminded of enough. I have spent so many years hustling and trying to climb the ladder. But what ladder am I climbing, exactly? It reminds me I should wait for instructions on which ladder, if any, I should scale!"

"Exactly," Phillip said with a grin. "More often than not, the best thing to do is just be patient and trust the correct response will come. Ahmet suggested that whether we are trying to make decisions for us or for others, this concept of waiting and trusting is usually the wisest choice."

Juliette nodded and smiled as Phillip continued his story . . .

"After we talked for a few more minutes, Ahmet looked at me and said, 'How about an excursion through the desert—a little field trip? I think there are a few things you could learn out there. It will be more "off the beaten path" than your trip from the airport. We'll be back in an hour—and I think you will be amazed at what we'll find. It happens every time I venture out with someone.'

"I smiled. 'I'm game. I know once I leave here, I won't be seeing a desert for a long, long time, so I would love to see what's out there.'

"'Great,' said Ahmet. 'Let's go.'

"He walked me out the door and opened the garage, revealing a beautiful red open-air Jeep. I had a huge grin as I exclaimed, 'Ah, she's a beauty!'

"'Yes, indeed,' said Ahmet. 'Plus, it's the perfect choice for the desert. Jump in!'

"I climbed into the passenger seat as Ahmet settled in on the driver's side, slowly backed the vehicle out, and turned toward the vast desert. As we began driving, I noticed the variety of plants scattered through the area. 'I had no idea there was this much magnificent plant life growing in the desert!'

"'Lesson number one,' Ahmet said with a smile, 'slow and steady wins the race in nature. Some of these varieties are over one hundred years old. You'll never see the effort, but what you *will* see are the results—the plants just continue to grow.'

"'Interesting. So, you're saying we don't need to constantly *struggle* to make things happen. We can learn from nature and simply be still, knowing everything will happen at the right time, like it does here in the desert.'

"Ahmet nodded. 'Precisely. God's timing will always be perfect. If we can remember this and simply allow life to unfold, it will save us a lot of effort, stress, and frustration.'"

Juliette excitedly stopped Phillip in his narration. "There it is again, that concept of *allowing things to unfold!*"

Phillip grinned. "I knew you would like that. You'll also like this next thing Ahmet told me . . ."

Phillip went back into his story. "Ahmet would constantly call my attention to things in the desert to support the philosophy he was sharing. For example, we came to an oasis, and he pointed to the body of water and said, 'Another example of effortless power. Who would think water could exist in this massive bed of sand? But it does—and it lies there so peacefully!' He added, 'Again, nature shows us the lesson that all things are possible, and without force!'

"I smiled at Ahmet. 'This is exactly what I needed to hear. I have always considered myself a person of faith, but I can see that I have spent a lot of unnecessary time and effort over the last three years struggling to "make things happen." In reality, I was just going against the wise ways of nature—and making things more difficult for myself—by doing so.'

"A smile spread across Ahmet's face. 'Phillip, if you have learned that, then you will forever be changed. Learning how to trust—regardless of how circumstances appear—is a way of thinking few people truly understand.'

"Just then, Ahmet pointed to the distance. 'There's another item of interest, Phillip: Can you see that outline? It's probably twenty miles from here, but in the desert, there is nothing to block your view, almost like you can see infinitely far.'

"'Yes, Ahmet, I can. Is that . . . the Great Pyramid of Giza?' I asked incredulously.

"Ahmet smiled. 'Yes, and it holds a part of your last lesson in the desert. It is one of the Seven Wonders of the Ancient World, as I am sure you know.'

"I nodded and waited anxiously for his next words.

"'Think about this, Phillip: it took twenty thousand workers over twenty years to build this magnificent structure. Can you believe that?'

"I shook my head. 'Incredible.'

"'It's true,' Ahmet said. 'But no one rushed the project! First, they *believed* it would happen, and then they simply, slowly, steadily moved forward. The result is what most people would call a miracle. Yet, I understand, and now you do too, this is simply an example of what we are all capable of. Call it a miracle, or call it living up to our potential, but regardless, we must understand it is a matter of choosing to believe something is possible—for ourselves and for others— and then patiently staying the course to completion. In your case, it may mean trusting there is a much bigger plan at work through this whole lottery ordeal—and just being patient until that plan is revealed.'"

Phillip then said to Juliette, "I was stunned. He was right—and it all made total sense to me."

Juliette smiled. "I wouldn't have thought the lottery could ever end up teaching a person these kinds of lessons, but then again, as you said earlier, the best lessons often come from the most unexpected places. The more I hear about this journey of yours, the more confident I am that everything I have gone through has prepared me for the times ahead."

"Hard to believe, isn't it?" Phillip said with a grin. "Lessons like these—or classrooms like these, as you said—are around us all the time, but many times we don't see them until a tragedy makes us see them."

Juliette thought for a moment. "Or maybe we can often learn to find them without having to go through the tragedies. Of course, I understand difficult situations will continue to occur in our lives. But Ahmet said if we get quiet and listen, we can 'hear' the answers we need, and then act on them in a nonreactive way—which we couldn't do if we were trying to use force. At that point, we simply need to remain patient and persistent, with a calm, courageous belief that our results will manifest at the right time. It's just a wonderful way of dealing with life."

"Great point," Phillip said with a gentle smile. "I believe Ahmet was also saying the more we act in that effortless, trusting manner, the simpler it is to do it again and again until it becomes a part of our being. In fact, Ahmet told me that after a while, we start becoming acutely aware of when we are on the verge of making an impulsive or forceful choice, so we can then step back and choose wisely and intuitively."

"I understand," Juliette said with an affirming nod. "I wish I had known all of this sooner."

"Me too," Phillip said, shaking his head. "But again, that's when we must trust the perfect timing of it all."

Juliette nodded and smiled as Phillip began concluding his story of desert wisdom.

"After we got back in the Jeep, Ahmet turned the vehicle around, and we drove away from the pyramid, back to his home. He remained quiet for a few seconds and then said calmly, 'Phillip, there's one more lesson from the desert, and I would be remiss if I didn't point it out to you.'

"I looked at Ahmet pensively as the sandy Egyptian landscape began passing by faster.

"He then spoke loudly to drown out the sound of the wind and the roar of the engine: 'We have talked much about peace, lack of struggle, patience, and trust. But it is important to remember that all of these must be woven together with the thread of simplicity. Living out here, I have learned how little is available, and consequently how little I need to be happy. Truthfully, I have now learned how little I even *want*—but those things I want, I place great value on.'

"I nodded as Ahmet continued.

"'If you do not find and consistently appreciate what's truly important in life, then the wisdom I have shared today will be an inadequate aid on your journey—you will constantly reach for the unreachable to make yourself happy, and you will come up short again and again. You'll *never* have enough, and feelings of discontentment, frustration, and disappointment will be your constant companions.' Ahmet then added firmly, yet with compassion, 'Phillip, I have no doubt you *know* what is most important in your life . . .'

"I nodded in agreement. I was stunned and yet incredibly relieved by how this wise man had so accurately assessed my deep needs and addressed them one by one. I leaned back comfortably, realizing the irony of the situation—it had taken me, a quarter-of-a-billion-dollar lottery winner, going across the world to the beauty of the desert to remind myself what was important in life: faith, peacefulness, compassion, generosity, and simplicity. It was crystal clear that these precious things are always available, deeply impactful—and they could never be taken away from me. I couldn't help but smile, and as we sped through the massive desert, I instinctively threw up my hands and shouted, 'WOO-HOO!'

"Yes, I was now understanding what Patrick O'Rourke meant when he said this journey would permanently change me. In fact, I was already changed, and as the warm Sahara breeze blew through my hair, I felt free—freer than I had ever felt before . . ."

CHAPTER 9

Juliette leaned back, exhaled deeply, and shook her head. She said with a grin, "I feel like I was traveling in the desert with the two of you! It must have been exhilarating to not only be speeding through the Sahara, but to be taking in everything Ahmet was sharing with you. After an enlightening time like that, what *more* could Ahmet possibly share with you?"

Phillip smiled. "It certainly *was* enlightening. But there was definitely more to come . . .

"When we returned to Ahmet's home, my euphoria hadn't faded. 'Ahmet,' I asked, 'how did you learn these things? Was it through your own difficulties, or did God just give you a good ol' healthy dose of wisdom?'

"'Have a seat at the kitchen table,' he said softly. 'I want to share something with you.'

"As I sat down, Ahmet began preparing lamb, adding some mint jelly to the meat and letting it sit for a few moments. He then brought some fresh orange juice to the table.

"'Here's a little juice to rehydrate you,' he offered with a smile. 'The desert takes it out of you, for sure.'

"I nodded and sipped on the tasty nectar while Ahmet cut up the lamb, placed it on two plates, and brought them over to the table. Once he was seated, he gestured for me to begin eating. As I did so, he spoke . . .

"'Phillip, when I told you I was depressed as a young man, it was because my parents were killed in the Great War with our neighboring country, Sudan.'

"I was obviously shocked, but Ahmet continued.

"'It happened when I was only sixteen. The soldiers came one day and took them both while I hid under the bed—they never even knew I was there. They burned the home upon leaving, and I was barely able to escape through a back window.'

"Ahmet put his head in his hands, visibly shaken. 'Still today I regret that I did not fight for them, but if I had tried, surely the barbarians would have killed me. They took my parents away, and I found out later they were forced to work ten, fifteen hours per day in the desert heat with little food. Soon after, my mother died, as she was already not in good health. My father was so angry that, though he continued to work for the tyrants, he constantly waited for the chance to take revenge on them. Unfortunately, another slave went to the king and told him what my father was planning. My father was thrown into solitary confinement, and he eventually died there before I could ever see him again. My understanding is that he passed away from a broken heart.'

"Ahmet continued, 'From the day my parents were taken, I wandered the streets. There was nothing left of our house, and I had nowhere to go. Fortunately, my uncle in Alexandria eventually heard of my plight, and he and my aunt found me and took me into their home. My uncle helped me get a job, and I found a way to continue my education through high school and then to college. I worked tirelessly to pay for my schooling because I knew it was what I had to do— my father always told me the only thing that separated successful people from others was education, and I was determined to succeed. Eventually I graduated, then received a master's degree, then a doctorate, and then I came back to the university as a professor. At that point, my life continued to improve, and I eventually met Patrick, as I shared with you.'"

Recalling the intensity of that conversation, Phillip shook his head and said to Juliette, "I looked at Ahmet and attempted to console him, but he held up his hand as if to stop me. 'Phillip,' he said, 'the point of all this is that I was never *given* wisdom. Like you, I learned as I went, gradually transforming my pain into potent, valuable lessons. I began understanding the power in the traits I shared with you, and I knew they were keys to living a happier life. I opened myself to new teachings without getting in my own way. I began trusting that life was working on my behalf, and miraculously, my view of the world changed. I now believe everything that occurs in my life is happening *for* me—instead of *to* me, and it makes all the difference.'

"I nodded. 'I understand, Ahmet. You can't imagine how your heartfelt story has touched me. It has helped me see that everything I have gone through has readied me for a path I couldn't have foreseen, but one which will take me precisely where I need to go. What you have shared with me, including the wisdom from our time in the desert, has shown me life as it can be—as it *will* be for me.'

"Ahmet nodded, leaned back, and smiled. 'I am very happy to hear this, Phillip. Let's finish our dinner, and you can retire here for the night—I have a room prepared for you at the end of the hall. You are welcome to stay as long as you'd like, but I am sure you are eager to get to the next stop on your journey. I know the lessons I have shared with you have not fallen on deaf ears. Indeed, I do believe your life is changing.'

"I smiled. 'I think I could stay in this beautiful place for weeks, but as you say, I have more to learn, so I will depart tomorrow. I will have a layover in Switzerland for a night, so I will have even more time to rest. I'm grateful for everything, Ahmet, and I will never forget you or our time together.'

"We stood, and Ahmet firmly clasped my hand, looked me squarely in the eyes, and offered, 'Feel free to come back any time, Phillip. I feel a deep kinship of spirit with you, and it has been a gift to have you here.'

"I nodded appreciatively and then walked down the short hallway to my room for the night. After I prepared for bed, instinctively I offered a short prayer of gratitude for what I had learned so far—and promptly fell sound asleep when my head hit the pillow."

CHAPTER 10

Phillip seemed to recall the details of his trip so clearly, it was as if he had just returned from the journey.

"I awoke around ten o'clock the next morning to the sound of a car engine running softly. Looking through the open window, I saw Karim stepping out of his vehicle as he looked up and spotted me in my groggy, disheveled state.

"'Hey, are you coming down, my friend? You've got a flight to catch!' he called out with a big grin.

"I managed a smile, rubbed my eyes, and then yelled back, 'Sorry, Karim, I overslept. Guess I should have set my alarm, but it felt so good to finally get some rest. Give me a few minutes.'

"He smiled and walked up to the front door, which was open, as if Ahmet was expecting him. Having known Ahmet for many years, Karim stepped inside and sat down in a chair in the den to wait for me. I took a quick shower, then gathered my belongings and headed down the hall with my suitcase. When I stepped into the kitchen, fully expecting to see Ahmet, I instead saw a note on the counter addressed to me:

Dear Phillip,

I had to go into Cairo early this morning, much to my chagrin. As I told you, I would rather herd angry goats than fight that traffic! Nevertheless, the animals need food, and since I have more guests coming in this afternoon, morning was the only time I knew I could go. I have left some bread, cheese, and a few bottles of water for your journey.

It has been an honor to serve you. I hope the time we spent together was helpful, as it was certainly an enjoyable experience for me. I learn from every person I teach, and having you as a student was indeed a highlight this year.

I trust the knowledge you take back will make life better and happier for you and anyone else around you. The traits and gifts I talked about are timeless, and you will learn to harness them and thus become stronger as the years go on.

Safe travels to America—and take care, my friend.

Ahmet

"I took the note, folded it, and put it in the pocket of my jeans. Then, grabbing the goodies that Ahmet had left for me, I walked into the den to meet Karim for our trip to the airport.

"'Ready to go, Phillip?' Karim asked with a big smile.

"'Ready as I'll ever be.' I shook my head and added, 'I never knew there was so much wisdom in the desert, but I certainly do now!'

"Karim looked at me in an approving way and said quietly, 'Yes, there is wisdom all around us, and the desert is no exception—especially with Ahmet as your guide.'

"I grinned. 'You can say that again.'

"We stepped out the front door and walked over to Karim's waiting car, and then I threw my suitcase into the back seat. As I plopped down next to him, Karim started the engine, and it occurred to me this magnificent journey was coming closer to an end. Never in my wildest dreams did I think I could learn so much about life—and myself—in such a short time.

"Karim winked at me as if he knew what I was thinking. He smiled, patted me affectionately on the shoulder, and guided the car into the vast Egyptian desert toward the distant airport.

"It was an uneventful ride back into Cairo. In fact, I slept most of the way, but when I periodically awoke, all I saw was the repeating scenery of sand and an occasional camel caravan."

"'Kind of like a trip back in time,' I said at one point to Karim.

"'Yes, it is. Egypt is a blend of the old and the new.' He shrugged and added, 'Quite frankly I am not sure the new is any better.'

"I nodded. 'I guess change is inevitable, but I think it was Mahatma Gandhi who said, "There is more to life than increasing its speed."'

"'Amen to that, my friend. Spoken with simplicity—I think you would fit in well with our club. Want to stay in Cairo?' He laughed.

"'Well, as much as I like the desert, I think I'll need to get back to the good old USA—although I am a little concerned about what to do when I get a craving for mint tea and a good lamb chop.' I smiled.

"Karim replied with a laugh, 'True. I guess you'll have to put in a special order with the New York street vendors!'

"Just then, looking ahead to his left, Karim saw the sign indicating our arrival at the Cairo airport. 'I am afraid it is time for us to part ways, my friend.' He pulled the car into the parking spot in front of the Egyptair sign, stepped out, and walked around to open the door for me.

"I took his outstretched hand, and as I got out of the car, I said, 'Thank you, Karim. I am grateful for all your help, and I hope we will see each other again— for some reason, I think we will.'

"Karim nodded, put his right hand over his heart, and replied, 'It would be a pleasure, Phillip.'

"I walked up to the airport entrance and turned one last time to see Karim now slowly backing out of the parking space. Glancing forward, he caught my eye and gave me one final wave, upon which I stepped inside the building to check in for my flight back to the USA.

"Yes, I was going home, but as David Cairns would soon show me high up in the Colorado mountains, the last lesson on this trek would be one I desperately needed. . ."

CHAPTER 11

The train had pulled out of Newbridge about fifteen minutes earlier, but Juliette was so engrossed in Phillip's story, she didn't realize the train had moved at all.

Looking pensively at Phillip, she felt compelled to ask him a question that had been increasingly on her mind. "Phillip, do you think you could ever go back to Chloe after what she did?"

Phillip's reply was firm: "I could not."

Juliette's expression remained neutral as she said, "I know how much you loved her, but I also know how much she hurt you."

He shrugged. "It's not as much about what she did," he replied. "It's more about who I have become."

Intrigued, Juliette leaned in as Phillip continued.

"Chloe is like everyone else in that she just wants to be happy—and I can appreciate that. Being with me would not make her happy anymore. Spiritually and emotionally, I have now become the person I knew down deep I always wanted to be, and she has become the person she never wanted to be. I wish her the best, but my life is no longer compatible with hers."

Phillip looked out the window as if pondering some regret. "Of course, I wish it had been different, but as you and I have discussed over the last two hours, things have turned out just *right*. I must not get in the way of letting my life's plan be revealed."

Juliette smiled softly. "You are a good man, Phillip Westford. I don't know anyone else with your principles and your desire for goodness. . . for all. I am grateful to have met you."

"I take that as the highest compliment—however unworthy I may feel to receive it—thank you." He smiled. "Now let me ask *you* a question," he said with a sly grin. "Where do you see *your* journey taking you?"

She sighed, leaned back, and replied with a smile, "Well, of course I am simply going to allow everything to unfold and keep my hands off the steering wheel of life as much as possible." Phillip laughed heartily. She continued, "But . . . I also know from this conversation and from the lessons you learned that it's important to set goals first—then trust the proper results will come."

Phillip nodded tentatively as he wondered what was coming next.

Juliette took a deep breath and blurted out, "Phillip, I have a burning desire to start my own TV talk show. I want to interview women who have dealt with difficulties as I have and encourage them to keep pressing on to reach their dreams. I had thought about it before, but since what happened to me—whoops, I mean *for* me—in New York," she said with a smile, "I feel as if I am now prepared more than ever to do this show. I would call it something like *Juliette Has Found Another Jewel*, and I would give these deserving women the exposure and opportunities I never had."

Phillip applauded and smiled. "Bravo, Juliette. Sounds like a show that will impact the world!"

"Really? You think so?" She blushed.

"Absolutely."

Juliette crossed her arms, leaned back, and laughed. "Well, once I raise about a million dollars, I may just do that."

Phillip replied without hesitation. "There are no shortages of money, just shortages of ideas and courage, Juliette."

Juliette looked into Phillip's eyes and saw reflected in them her own sense of belief and determination. She felt he understood her plight unlike anyone had before. She pushed her hair back and looked away. Anxious to change the subject, she asked, "So, Phillip, what happened when you left Egypt?"

Phillip grinned, fully aware she had intentionally shifted the course of the conversation.

"Okay, if you insist . . .

"I took the flight from Cairo to Denver, and fortunately, on my layover I found a quaint Swiss hotel near the airport to spend the night. It worked out well because I grabbed dinner at a nice German restaurant down the street, was able to have a full night's sleep, and was easily back on a flight to Colorado by mid-morning.

"When we deplaned, true to form, there was a man at the airport to greet me, holding a sign with my name on it. He wore a name tag that said simply 'Big D,' and he was a lean, fit-looking fellow with a scruffy gray beard, piercing blue eyes, and a long, gray ponytail. Wearing jeans and a light green windbreaker, he had a youthful, energetic appearance, although it turned out he was nearly seventy years old!

"I stepped over to introduce myself and he cheerfully asked, 'Ready to hit the road, Phillip? We've got some steep mountains ahead!' He had an extra dose of enthusiasm, and I immediately liked him.

"'Ready when you are, Big D!'

"I struggled to keep up with this spry gentleman as he walked briskly out to the parking lot. When we reached the row where he had parked, he pointed to an old, red Volkswagen van.

"'That would be mine, sir!' he proudly said.

"It didn't surprise me, because 'Big D' had a free-spirited way about him. We put my suitcase in the back of the van, closed the doors, buckled up, and headed off to the mountains.

"I wondered aloud, 'So, I understand we're headed pretty far north—like as far north as Colorado goes, I think I was told.'

"The man shrugged and replied jovially, 'The altitude is only about two miles—just enough to get a good nosebleed.'

"I smiled, shook my head, and then asked curiously, 'By the way, is "D" short for something?'

"He chuckled. 'Can't slip anything past you. It's short for David.'

"I wrinkled my brow. 'David?'

"'Yes, like David Cairns. That's me.'

"'So, if you're David Cairns, then . . .'

"He interrupted me by laughing and holding up his hand. 'If you're wondering why I didn't send a driver like Ahmet and those other guys do, that's not my style. Anyway, I've got plenty of time these days since the fire, so who needs to hire a driver?'

"Puzzled, I looked at him and asked, 'The fire?'

"He shrugged nonchalantly and began chattering. 'Well, yeah, but it's okay. All is slowly getting back to normal. We can talk about that later. So, how did you like Egypt? Pretty hot out there, huh? I don't know how Ahmet does it. Or José for that matter—Mexico is just about as bad with the heat. In fact, it may be worse down there with all that humidity. Then again, they don't have twenty-foot snow drifts in Cairo and Cancún like we do, so I guess it's all a trade-off.'

"He laughed, and I couldn't help but laugh along with this contagiously happy man.

"We made small talk as we drove for the next three hours, but mostly I just stared out at the spectacular mountain scenery. It was like nothing I had ever seen. With a grin, I commented, 'Well, this isn't Springfield, Missouri, I'll tell you that!'

"David laughed. 'Well, you got that right—although I do like Springfield. I've been there several times.'

"I smiled and shook my head. 'Small world. I should know that by now. In fact, if there's one thing I've learned on this trip, it's just how small this world is.'

"At that moment, David pulled the van into the parking lot of a modest Alpine-style motel which looked like it had about twenty rooms all on one level. 'Speaking of small worlds, we've reached mine,' he said casually.

"I looked at David in obvious surprise and he countered with an easy, reassuring grin. 'Okay, okay, it's not quite as nice as Ahmet's place, but it'll do for now.'

"*Does he . . . live here*? I wondered.

"David saw my skepticism and offered, 'Let's go inside the restaurant. I know you're famished, and I can get Margaret to make us some of her legendary stuffed trout. I think you'll like it.'

"I nodded in tentative approval, still unsure of my surroundings.

"When we stepped into the motel lobby, the young lady at the front desk cheerfully greeted us. 'Hi, David, got a friend today?'

"David nodded, motioned toward me, and replied, 'Suzie, may I introduce my friend Phillip!'

"She looked at me as if she was genuinely glad I was there. 'Welcome, Phillip—it's great to meet you!'

"David chimed in, 'I was going to introduce him to Margaret's famous stuffed Colorado trout. Since I'm a resident here now, I can vouch for it.'

"*Okay, he* does *live here*, I thought. *I know Patrick wouldn't steer me wrong, but this is . . .*

"The perky young woman interrupted my thought as she gestured to the next room where the restaurant was located, saying, 'He'll love it—enjoy, fellas!'

"We walked through the open glass door and into the small dining room. There were six simple tables with red and white checkered tablecloths and only two customers—an older husband and wife—sitting at one of the other tables.

"The more I thought about it, the more I wondered what I was doing there—and what I was doing with David Cairns. *Could this guy be an imposter? Was somebody playing a joke on me—maybe Patrick?*

"We sat down, and almost immediately, the waitress—a freckle-faced woman with curly red hair in her mid-twenties—approached us.

"'Hi, Big D, having your usual today?'

"'Yes, indeed. An order of Margaret's Best—and one for my friend, please.'

"'Right away. And I'll bring you guys each a big glass of fresh lemonade—Margaret just made it.'

"Despite my increasing uneasiness, I managed a smile as I looked at her and said, 'That sounds perfect. Thank you.'

"The waitress wrote down the order, smiled back at us, and walked toward the other side of the restaurant.

"Finally, I couldn't handle it anymore. 'Okay, David, I've got to ask . . .'

"Sensing what was coming, David playfully hit his forehead with an open palm. 'Ah, you wanted the burger instead, didn't you?'

"'No, no, it's just—I've never known someone who lived in a motel. You *do* live here, right?'

"For the first time, I saw David's enthusiasm wane. He nodded and said, 'Well, the short answer is . . . yes.'

"I leaned back and crossed my arms, still puzzled. 'Well, I have to say, it's really . . .'

"David interrupted. 'Yes, it's really . . . a blessing. It's a blessing to have this place.'

"My mouth hung open. Now I was *really* confused.

"'Phillip, let me show you something,' David said, slowly pulling out two 3 x 5 photographs from his jacket pocket. One of them he laid face down on the table.

"I looked at him with intrigue as David gestured toward the photo and calmly said, 'Turn it over.'

"I reached down tentatively and flipped the photograph over. It was of the most magnificent mountain homes I had ever seen. It must have been ten thousand square feet, and it was nestled into a beautiful mountainside. All around the house were animals— dogs, cats, horses, goats, cows.

"Sitting on the front porch was . . . David Cairns.

"Still puzzled, I looked at him and said, 'It's a beautiful place, but I don't know what this means, David.'

"Without responding, David calmly put the second photograph face down in front of me. Once again, he motioned to me to pick it up. I reached for the photo and turned it over slowly. What I then saw made me recoil in shock. Before I could speak, David Cairns cut in.

"'Yes, it *was* a beautiful place. It burned to the ground a year ago,' he said solemnly.

"I looked again at the destroyed home and saw next to it the charred remains of a camper, two cars, and several pieces of machinery. But those burned remnants were all that was left of the once breathtaking dwelling.

"'What happened? Was this your home, David?' I asked incredulously.

"'Built it with my own two hands,' he said evenly.

"'What about the animals? Did they survive?'

"'They made it out—with a little help from me,' he said with a gentle smile.

"At this point, I was shaking my head. 'I am so sorry, David. May I ask . . . what happened?'

"David looked away as if he was about to evade the question, then took a deep breath and looked back at me.

"'It started out as a beautiful Colorado day, just like today. I was in the woods hunting about a mile from my house, and suddenly a freak thunderstorm rolled in. I decided to head back home, and just as I reached a hill overlooking my property, I saw a huge bolt of lightning hit the house—immediately the flames began engulfing one side of the home. I threw down my rifle and started sprinting, but the fire was spreading so quickly that I knew I would never get there in time to save the house. I managed to get to the animals while the structure continued to burn, and I barely got them out before the fire was unbearable. It was unbelievably hot—and even now I still have burns over both my arms.'

"David rolled up his sleeves to show me, and I tried to keep my face neutral at the sight of the intense burns.

"'I just can't believe it,' I said.

"David shook his head and smiled. 'Yeah, me neither, my friend. I never knew a fire could spread so fast. After I got all the animals to a pen safely away from the house, I tried to get inside to rescue whatever items I could. The fire was so hot that it kept me away, so all I could do was stand there and watch the home that I was so proud of . . . fade into memory.'

"Just then, the waitress showed up with two large plates of trout, french fries, and homemade macaroni and cheese. David's expression lifted as he said to the young woman, 'Now *that's* a lunch!'

"Still dumfounded, I managed a smile as I accepted my plate. 'Thank you, ma'am. It looks delicious.'

"We began eating our lunch in quiet, and after a moment, David broke the silence.

"'After the tragedy, it affirmed to me the incredible goodness that lies within most people. I had moved to the area five years prior, and I had spent most of my time working in solitude, building the house. Even so, I still managed to meet a lot of the locals because I was often in town here buying supplies, eating at little restaurants, and just generally going about my business.'

"'It does seem like a friendly place,' I offered.

"'It's more than just friendliness,' David countered quickly. He paused, took a deep breath, and then said, 'Let me tell you a story, Phillip.'

"I took a sip of my lemonade and leaned in with keen interest as David began.

"'Twenty years ago, I was traveling quite a bit. I didn't have a great deal of money, but I had dreams of seeing the world, and I didn't want to look back with regrets. Plus, I had just gone through a painful divorce, and I suppose I wanted to try and "find myself," as they say. So, I quit my job as a technical analyst at a large company, took out a loan, and set off to travel the globe for a year.'

"David went on, 'At one point in my journey, I had left China, headed west, and I stopped in Greece for an overnight layover. I ventured out into a beautiful part of town, but the people there didn't speak much English. None of the signs were in English, either—including the menus posted outside the restaurants—and I was starving. I was standing outside a café, trying to understand any part of the menu, and I must've looked horribly frustrated. At that moment, a woman walked up behind me and tapped me on the shoulder. With her long, gray locks and deeply lined face, she looked in her early eighties. She was small in stature, slightly stooped, and she wore clothes that were brightly colored but were old and tattered. I assumed she was a beggar, especially when she opened her mouth, pointed to it, and said "ah" like she was trying to tell me she wanted food.

"'I shook my head, shrugged my shoulders, and said, "No money." Just then, the old woman shook *her* head, pointed again to her mouth, and motioned for me to follow her. I did notice she seemed kind, and for whatever reason, I trusted her, so I followed her. We went through alleys and around buildings, and occasionally she would look back, smile, and motion to keep up, which I did.

"'Then after about five minutes of walking through the city, we came to the back of an old building. Once again, she turned to make sure I was still there, then began walking up a flight of about thirty black, metal stairs. I tentatively began my ascent behind her. Finally, we reached the top of the stairs, and the older woman turned again, nodded, and opened the door for me to enter a brightly lit, highly energetic, large room filled with people.

"'As I walked into the place with her now beside me, I stopped in shock. There just a few feet in front of me was the most magnificent buffet of Greek food you could possibly imagine—and people inside were seated, laughing together and thoroughly enjoying their meals. I turned and looked at the woman, beaming now as she pointed once again to her open mouth and said, "Ah!"

"'I couldn't help it: I reached down and hugged her as tears of gratitude rolled down my cheeks.'

"David finished by saying, 'We walked through the buffet line and loaded our plates up, and then sat down amongst maybe fifty other people. But before we began eating, the old woman bowed her head and said a beautiful blessing in her native Greek language. We ate without speaking, then we both stood and walked out the door together. Outside the restaurant, she gently clasped my hand, smiled, then turned and walked away, and I never saw her again.'

"'That's unbelievable,' I said to David. 'She was like an angel from heaven.'

"David seemed to regain his enthusiasm as he leaned back and clapped his hands. 'Yes! Even though you would never believe it based on her outward appearance, she *was* like an angel—which is precisely what the people here have been to me. They have been *my* guardian angels. So yes, it is a bunch of nice people, but it is much more. They understand the power of genuine, unrestricted generosity. They have been willing to help me in ways I could have never imagined. I lost everything in the fire—my wallet, my clothes, my car . . . everything.'"

Phillip shook his head, grinned, and said to Juliette, "I started to interject, but he was not finished schooling me.

"David continued, 'Phillip, here's my point: when I lost everything, the community rallied around me in a way you would not believe. One couple let me borrow their car for as long as I needed it. One person walked up and gave me five hundred dollars in cash. One person gave me a gift card for one thousand dollars to go buy new clothes. Another gave me a pair of shoes because I didn't have any after the fire. Many of these people didn't even know me! Like the Greek woman, these folks have asked for nothing in return—they just wanted to help.'

"As if I hadn't heard enough, David pointed toward the lobby. 'Do you remember Suzie at the front desk?'

"I nodded meekly, wondering what was coming next.

"'Her family owns the place. They told me I could stay here at no charge for as long as I want, plus all my meals are free. As I have chosen to rebuild my house, this could take years—especially with the insurance company unmercifully dragging out my settlement. It's already been a year, and I don't know if I will continue to stay here during the entire reconstruction, but it's an incredibly generous offer, and I am grateful for the opportunity to be here. I really have everything I need, thanks to this community.'

"I sat silently as David added, 'I grew up in southern Colorado, and living in a middle-class family with good values, I felt like I understood what was important in life. But I learned through my time with Ahmet, Patrick, and José what is *most* important. Strangely enough, in many ways I feel I was prepared for this disaster, although I wouldn't have been if it weren't for the years with those men.'

"I leaned back and exhaled deeply, grabbing my head in disbelief at how I had just been justifiably humbled by this great man. I had been taught a lesson about judging people and situations on appearances rather than taking the time and effort to learn more about them. Ironically, being judged by others on what people assumed *my* life was like as a lottery winner was one of the things I despised—yet without realizing it, I had been doing the same to David.

"I then asked David what he meant when he said he wouldn't have been this way if it weren't for those years with Patrick, José, and Ahmet.

"He thought for a few seconds and then said, 'Well, first, let me say that we all have an innate ability to rise above our circumstances and use our pain to fuel us to a better way of thinking and living—but we don't even typically scratch the surface of our potential. When I met Patrick, his strong faith and constant encouragement allowed me to see how capable I was. Ahmet and José helped me in a very similar way.'

"'How did you meet Patrick?' I asked.

"David smiled. 'I stopped in Dublin toward the end of my year of travel, and I "coincidentally" met Patrick at a coffee shop there, and we just began talking. The longer we talked, the more I realized this man had a spirit of courage and compassion that can only come from a life forged through deep challenges.'

"I nodded my agreement as David went on, 'Then Patrick started telling me about meeting with Ahmet each week, and I knew I wanted to join these men and find out more about them even though I was scheduled to leave Ireland in a few days. Patrick agreed to the meeting with Ahmet, and when I first joined them, it was as if we had known each other forever. Over the next few days, I fell in love with the people, the rich culture, and the history—and I savored the time I was able to spend with these wise people. Fortunately, they felt the same about me, and I was so happy in this new place that I moved permanently to Dublin. Once I relocated, the three of us had so many enlightening discussions—our conversations sometimes lasted five or six hours, and I could feel myself becoming wiser and more inspired as we then began writing books together. I felt like I was doing exactly what I was called to do! José joined us after we developed the global leadership program, and the talent and insight he brought to our group took my understanding of an empowering, compassionate life to a whole new level.

"'In fact,' he finished, 'I guess you could say on this trek to find myself, I did just that—by *losing* myself in service to others.'"

Phillip looked at Juliette and noticed how riveted she still was to his story, so he continued, "I had heard from Ahmet and José that David's gifts had a tremendous impact on shaping the world. So I asked David what they meant by that.

"David threw back his head and laughed. 'Well, it's a bit of an exaggeration. But here's what I guess they mean . . .

"'For a period of my life—the time I worked with Patrick, Ahmet, and José—I was wealthy, like I hear you are, my friend.'

"I suddenly felt even more a sense of camaraderie with this kindhearted man.

"He continued, 'My parents invested well, and when they passed away, they left everything to me. It was incredibly generous. They were philanthropists, and the only thing they asked was that I use the money to make the world a better place.'

"My eyes widened as I listened carefully.

"'I invested the money, and it grew beyond my wildest dreams. But here is one of the things I gratefully realized through all my time with those gentlemen: if used wisely, money is a wonderful tool. You can use it to open doors, and you can use it to help impact people's lives on unprecedented levels. For my part, I used the money to build things.'

"Noting my look of curiosity, David smiled and then continued.

"'Whenever we went into a country to meet with the leaders, if they had limited resources, I promised we would help them help their people. I used the money I had been blessed with to invest in the greatest needs each of those countries had. Maybe it was building roads or schools, or providing them with better water or energy sources. So while our group went in and *talked* with people about ruling or leading compassionately, we also backed it up by providing them with tangible improvements to make their lives and their countries better. I guess you could call it sowing seeds.'

"I nodded and smiled in awe.

"'With each of the countries we served,' David said, 'we were able to win over hearts and minds to a nobler way of thinking and leading—while also physically improving their nations. So, I suppose you could say we were changing the world, to an extent.' He laughed.

"I shook my head as I realized I had never heard of generosity at the level David was describing—and it made me want to be like that. I also now understood that all the work these men had done to courageously help improve the world for us all—was totally unseen and unknown by the general population.

"Before I could respond, David added a comment that left me amazed: 'Since I chose to commit most of my money to the projects of the countries I just told you about, my financial status has dramatically changed. I have enough money to support my modest lifestyle, and that's all I want. Looking back, I wouldn't change a thing. At this point in my life, I have complete satisfaction in knowing the money went to making the world a better place—just like my parents asked me to do. Plus, what I have been given from the people in this community feels like ten times more than what I gave away during all those years.'

"I sat back in my chair, letting David's words sink in. His philosophy resonated with me so much. Not only had I learned about the power of being magnanimous, but I had been presented a remarkable lesson on humility. Here was David Cairns, a once wealthy man who had influenced powerful leaders all over the globe—and now he was content to live anonymously and without fanfare in a small lodge in the Rocky Mountains. Oddly enough, I couldn't help but feel envious. My heart sank as I remembered the same kind of peaceful, simple days with Chloe, before the lottery win.

"What David was expressing—his carefree, content, grateful attitude toward life now—was exactly what I longed for. . .

"Just then, the waitress stopped by, and we tried to pay her for the lunch, but she refused the money. With a grin, she wagged her finger at us. 'You know the rules, David. You don't pay—and neither do your guests.'

"David smiled and nodded, but as she walked away, he placed a ten-dollar bill on the table as a gratuity.

"The next two days were a blur of activity. We hiked through the mountains, fished in beautiful Colorado streams, had wonderful meals, and all the while we engaged in fantastic conversation. I had the opportunity to meet many of the people in the community whom David had told me about, and as he shared with me, they were inspiring and warm—including all the staff at the motel.

"On the morning of my departure, David smiled and said, 'You know, I think you learned the lessons here very well, Phillip. You're welcome to stick around longer, but I'm guessing after Mexico, Egypt, and Colorado, you're ready to get back home and into your own bed—although you must admit, the beds here are mighty comfortable.'

"I grinned. 'You're right about the beds, but I will have to say, I've already found myself waking up each morning wondering what country I'm in!'

"David threw back his head and laughed.

"After a quick breakfast, I thanked my gracious hosts at the inn, and David and I began the trip down the winding mountain roads back to Denver. The drive was filled with more lively conversation and more life lessons from 'D.' I eagerly took in every word.

"As we finally arrived at the departure terminal, I stepped out of the car, grabbed my suitcase, and thanked David from the bottom of my heart. 'I'll never forget this. Thank you.'

"David smiled. 'It's been a pleasure. As they say, any friend of Patrick's . . . is, well, you know.' We both laughed."

Just then, Juliette broke in excitedly, "This just gets better and better. I can't wrap my brain around the fact that you had the chance to meet all these incredibly wise people. I mean, David Cairns sounds like a one-of-a-kind person—how generous! So . . . what happened when you got back to New York?"

Phillip paused, looked out the window, then looked back at Juliette and shook his head. "This, my friend, is where it really gets interesting, and I think you'll soon understand why I am on this train . . ."

CHAPTER 12

Juliette smiled and leaned back as Phillip began sharing the last of his fantastic journey.

He said with a broad smile, "I can't tell you much about the flight home from Colorado because I was so exhausted, I fell asleep as soon as we took off, and I didn't wake up until we landed in New York."

Juliette giggled. "I bet. I'm tired just *hearing* about all the traveling!"

Phillip laughed and then continued, "After grabbing my luggage, I went outside and waited for a taxi. For the next few moments, I just stood there in the line, reflecting on the different visits. All of those incredible conversations with such wise people— it was hard to comprehend how different I felt from when I left Patrick's that night in Manhattan. I had gone from being a lonely, sad, discouraged man to a renewed person with a vision for making the world a better place. In fact, I couldn't wait to share my stories with Patrick."

Juliette interjected, "I can just imagine you sitting down with Patrick and telling him how much of a difference *he* had made in your life by encouraging you to go on this journey."

"You're right, Juliette. In fact, even though it was already around seven o'clock in the evening, when I finally got a cab, I had the driver drop me off at Patrick's, rather than at my place because I wanted to tell him about the trip as quickly as possible!"

Juliette nodded and smiled as Phillip then recounted that evening.

"When the cab driver dropped me off at Patrick's apartment, I *ran* up the stairs, and then I knocked and waited. . .. After what seemed like minutes, Patrick opened the door, and when he saw it was me, he almost jumped in the air as he yelled, 'You're back, lad! Come inside and tell me all about it!'

"I knew I was smiling in a way I hadn't in years as I sat down at his kitchen table. Patrick brewed some wonderful tea, and then he joined me at the table with our two cups.

"'Now, my good man. Tell me . . .' he said with his soothing Irish accent I knew so well.

"I began, 'Patrick, I can't thank you enough. These men are undoubtedly—as you said—three of the wisest people in the world! I realized their wisdom reminded me of some fantastic conversations I used to have with an old friend of mine, Royce Holloway. I haven't talked with him in probably ten years, and the time with these gentlemen has inspired me to reconnect with him.'

"Patrick nodded and smiled in a surprisingly understanding way. Then as I began sharing stories with him about the different places I visited, his smile broadened. I couldn't stop talking about all the experiences I'd had. But suddenly, Patrick held up his hand as if to stop me.

"'Phillip, now I want to hear how the visits have changed you. What did you learn from these incredible people that will make your life different and the world better?'

"I stopped and thought. Although I had found incredible new information and ideas, I hadn't yet put it all together—but I would quickly find it wasn't hard to do. I just started speaking and realized how the concepts I learned were already now a part of me . . .

"'Patrick, what I learned most was this: we all have people, experiences, and things in our lives that we can be grateful for. But what happens to most of us—I know it did to me—is we start leaning heavily on those things or those people to make us happy. When we do, we become more and more dependent on those externals, whether it's a person or money or an item or anything else. Soon, our focus is all about keeping the variables within our grasp. It then becomes a constant struggle to try and hold on to what or who we think makes us happy. Yet, the reality is that we can't hold on, because life is ever-changing. Life is going to take us to places we don't always want to go. We will lose people. We will be lonely. We will be hurt, and we will have constant upheaval—including reversals of fortune. But when we can fully accept that we really have no control over these "bad things happening," then *that* understanding alone can bring us a great deal of peace.'

"I saw Patrick was smiling and listening intently as I continued.

"'We can then begin focusing on what we *do* have control over, which is making a generous difference in the lives of other people. When we decide *that* will be our focus, it's an internal conviction no one can take away or diminish. Not only that, but we also become rare in this world because very, very few people are able to adopt this philosophy.'

"'I am so proud. Keep going, my friend,' Patrick urged.

"'Patrick, it's clearer to me than ever that the opportunity to positively impact other people is the greatest chance we have for making ourselves happy. If we can focus on having a generous mindset in everything we do, there will be little time to think about how lonely or miserable or sad we are. Even though we will continue to feel those emotions, the act of helping others will bring us to see everything in a different way—a much better way. We will be changed, happier people.

"'*That*, I believe, is the ultimate secret, and it is one I am grateful beyond belief to fully understand.'

"I looked at Patrick to see a tear rolling down the cheek of the typically jovial Irishman, and when he spoke to me, it was with a strangely tight voice. 'Phillip, I knew these gentlemen had lessons that would help turn your life around. It's a gift indeed to be with people who have your best interest in mind—with no judgments, isn't it?'

"I nodded and smiled as Patrick slowly continued.

"'Now, my friend, there's one more thing I must share with *you*.'

"I braced myself as Patrick O'Rourke looked at me with a grave expression I hadn't yet seen from him . . ."

CHAPTER 13

With an anxious look, Juliette put up her hands and broke into Phillip's narration. "Okay, Phillip, please tell me nothing *bad* happened to Patrick. I feel so attached to him now . . . what was it he wanted to say to you?"

Phillip shook his head, reassuring her, then he continued, "Before he could tell me, my eyes caught sight of the time and I realized in surprise that we had been sitting together for over two hours.

"'Patrick, I am so sorry I've talked the whole time—I guess I'm just overwhelmed and excited with what this trip has done for me.'

"Patrick smiled, held up his hand, and shook his head gently.

"'No apology necessary. It's exactly what I was hoping to hear, my friend. But now, Phillip, I must tell you, my time in New York is over. I will be leaving this week to go back to Ireland. I was getting kind of used to it here, but my work is done—successfully, I might add.' Patrick winked. 'Now it is time to move on to my next assignment, and I am afraid I'm not looking forward to it nearly as much.'

"I cocked my head to the side and said, 'But . . . why, Patrick? And who sent you here? You never told me that.'

"'Let's just say, the world is full of guardian angels, Phillip.'

"I looked at Patrick in uncertainty.

"'*You* are my guardian angel?'

"Patrick smiled. 'Phillip, each of us is a guardian angel to others—or at least we *can* be. Every time we find someone who needs help—and we respond—we are fulfilling the role of an angel to that person. We are compassionately, selflessly, courageously showing love, often when there seemed to be no hope. It's what we are all sent here to do, and there is nothing that can fulfill us more.'

"He continued, 'As José shared with you, encouragement can come through our words. As Ahmet shared with you, often it is simply through our deep, conscious, authentic presence. Or as David reminded you, it can be by giving money or time or material things. As we develop an altruistic spirit of generosity, we intuitively know what is needed in each situation.

"'Every day, all around you, there are opportunities to be a guardian angel—in ways big and small. It may be to show words of reassurance to a frazzled clerk in a store or to simply be a listener to someone going through a painful family crisis. We may never even know what a difference we made to them, but sometimes it could mean *all* the difference.

"'For me, the most recent opportunity I had to minister has been with. . . you. I wanted to make sure you were able to get your life back on track. As I shared before, I understand the sharp pain of losing cherished people. You have such compassion, such empathy, such love to give . . . all of which the planet needs now more than ever. I couldn't bear to see it wasted.'

"I was stunned. 'Amazing. You, Ahmet, José, and David *were* guardian angels to me. In different ways, you all showed me kindness when I needed it most—and all of you believed in me!'

"Patrick smiled and nodded easily. 'Of course. And now that you understand the unwavering power of generosity, you can share it in so many ways with others. That, my friend, is where the real magic lies, as you now know.'

"I was filled then with deep gratitude, but I suddenly felt sad when I wondered if or when I would see this incredible man again.

"'So, where will you go next, Patrick?'

"Something in Patrick's voice changed as he answered, 'There is a small village outside of Cork, Ireland, that desperately needs help. The people are struggling there, and they don't know what to do. They had a natural disaster—a horrible flood—and there is minimal water or electricity, and people are homeless by the thousands. The government is trying its best, but it's clearly not enough. This little town, Covington, is uniquely important to me.' Patrick's voice shook as he added, 'My wife was from there, and I want to see what I can do to help—maybe something, maybe nothing. I'll be leaving tomorrow, and I don't know when I will be back.'

"'Let *me* help, Patrick,' I quickly chimed in.

"Patrick put up his hand and shook his head. 'This is not why I came to you, Phillip. There will be plenty of people and places who will need your help. I will handle this.' He managed a smile and then added, 'It's not my first rodeo, as I believe you say in America.'

"With tears in my eyes now, I looked at Patrick and offered, 'I'm so sorry. I have friends who have lived through natural disasters—and it was devastating.'

"I saw the stress on Patrick's face as he nodded and stood. 'Yes, well, I will see what I can do—I don't know. Anyway, I must get some rest now, as the days ahead will be long for me like the recent days have been for you. Good night, Phillip, and farewell. Do stay in touch.'

"With that, Patrick reached out and embraced me like a kindly grandfather would his grandson. Strangely, right then I felt a genuine love and concern from him that I cannot describe.

"'I will, Patrick, and thank you for everything,' I said, fighting back tears. 'How can I ever repay you?'

"'Use the wisdom you have gleaned and help where you see a need, my good friend. It's all that is necessary, and indeed, in the end, it's all that matters,' he said with a smile.

"I tried to speak but realized I was too emotional, and so I simply nodded in agreement. Reluctantly, I turned away, opened the door, walked into the cold, dark New York evening, and hailed a taxi back to my apartment, thinking I would never see Patrick O'Rourke again.

"Little did I know . . ."

CHAPTER 14

Juliette was also fighting back tears. "Phillip, this story . . . it's like a dream."

Phillip shook his head. "I wouldn't have believed it either if it didn't happen to me. In fact, I'm still not sure I believe it."

Juliette grew quiet, and she was obviously deep in thought. "Phillip," she finally asked, "Is *this* why you are headed to southern Ireland? To help Patrick in Covington?"

Phillip nodded slowly. "When I left Patrick's that night, I couldn't stop thinking about the massive task ahead of him or about the opportunity being placed in front of me to help, especially after Patrick saved my life—which I believe he did."

"You know," Juliette said, managing a smile, "this really *is* a train ride to happiness—for you, for the Covington community, for Patrick . . . and for me."

Phillip smiled. "Yes, I would certainly say it's the greatest ride of my life."

Their eyes turned to the window as they felt the train begin to slow down. A bellowing, cheerful voice echoed through the train, "Cork! All passengers prepare to disembark! Welcome to Cork!"

As each of them brought their focus back inside the car, Juliette's eyes met Phillip's. Realizing their amazing ride was about to end, she looked down, paused briefly, and gently turned the recorder's control to the "OFF" position.

Seconds later, the train stopped, and the two new friends stepped out onto the platform at their long-awaited destination.

The weather in Cork was spectacular—a beautiful blue sky greeted them, there were green fields as far as one could see, and the temperatures on the southern coast felt refreshingly milder than their point of embarkment.

The pair headed to get their luggage, and as they walked, Juliette quietly said, "Phillip, after spending time with you, I feel like I have met someone I desperately needed to know. I hope we can stay in touch back in the States."

Phillip smiled easily. "It would be a pleasure to spend more time with you, Juliette. Tonight, I present my check to the mayor of Covington, and I will be leaving in two days to fly back to New York. Any time you are in the area, I hope you'll look me up."

He reached into his jacket pocket and handed her a business card.

"Of course," she replied, accepting the card, and gently pushing her hair back from the soft breeze.

As they stood and waited for their luggage, Juliette asked Phillip, "Does Patrick have any idea you are giving money to the community?"

He shook his head. "Patrick doesn't even know I am here. He is scheduled to announce a fundraiser tonight when he speaks at the event. But only the mayor knows I am coming. It will all be televised, and it will be attended by thousands of people from what I've heard. It's a bit nerve-wracking." Phillip smiled.

Just then the luggage arrived. "I suppose this is goodbye," Juliette said with a poignant smile. "I wish you all the best tonight."

"You're welcome to come to the presentation," Phillip added. "I bet I could sneak you in." He winked.

Juilette smiled and shook her head. "I have more story than I could have imagined after all you shared with me. My job was to find and interview you—and you not only made my job easy but incredibly enjoyable too. I'll catch the event on TV and cheer you on while I am reviewing our recording. My deadline is twenty-four hours from now, so I must get busy—I hardly know where to start."

Phillip nodded, then reached out and hugged Juliette. Slowly pulling away, he added, "I will always remember this day, Juliette. I do hope our paths cross again soon—and I look forward to reading your article." He smiled, and Juliette nodded in understanding.

With that, the two parted ways, and Phillip headed for the taxi stand to catch a ride to his hotel. Juliette stayed behind and sat quietly in the train station coffee shop, listening to the unimaginable recording she now had in her possession and reflecting on the extraordinary hours she had experienced with Phillip Westford. Her heart began pounding uncontrollably. She knew she was sitting on a Pulitzer-worthy story.

Juliette stared blankly ahead, lost in thought, then calmly turned the recorder off and placed it in her purse.

Evening came, and Phillip began preparing for the night's big event. He envisioned the crowd and got excited thinking about the difference this money would make in so many lives. After putting the finishing touches on his wardrobe, he called for a cab. When it arrived, Phillip stepped in and casually said to the driver: "14 Drisner Street, Covington, please."

The car pulled away as the cabbie began making small talk in his strong Irish accent.

"Going to the town hall meeting tonight, eh? Quite a dreadful thing everyone went through, wasn't it?

Hopefully, something can be done, but who knows—could be twenty years before things are back to normal, if ever. They say some bigwig is coming in to lead the fundraising, but you know how that goes. It's all tragic, just tragic," he said cynically.

Phillip nodded but offered no response as the driver brought him the rest of the way to Covington. Once he arrived at the meeting hall, Phillip was greeted at the back door of the building by the mayor of Covington, a short, stocky man who offered a firm, heartfelt handshake.

"It's a blessing to have you here, Mr. Westford. You are going to change this community forever. Thank you from the bottom of my heart."

Phillip smiled and replied, "It's my pleasure, Mr. Mayor. Thank you for having me. When is Patrick due to speak?"

"At 7:35. I will open with a quick welcome and then introduce Patrick so he can share some encouragement. As we discussed, no one knows you will be donating the money—including Patrick."

"Very good," Phillip replied appreciatively.

At that moment, Juliette McKelvey, who had spontaneously decided to take a cab to Covington and witness the excitement, arrived at the front door of the meeting hall. Hoping her journalist credentials would get her into the sold-out event, she walked swiftly to the entrance.

"Hi, I'm with the press," she offered curtly, flashing her identification badge.

The young ticket agent looked at her with sympathy, shaking his head. "So sorry, Miss. It's closed. The hall is full, and no one else is allowed in—unless you're a resident of Covington."

"You don't understand, I *have* to be in there," she pleaded.

"Sorry, ma'am, you'll have to watch on the telly," he firmly replied.

"But . . ."

The man abruptly turned away as if he hadn't heard her, then closed the door, leaving Juliette in the cool Irish evening. With a sigh of exasperation, she dashed to the nearest pub, about two hundred yards away. Scanning the room, she spotted and then quickly claimed the last available seat at the bar in front of the television, which was tuned to the town hall meeting.

Keeping her eyes riveted to the screen, she told the waiting bartender, "A glass of your best red wine, please."

The man smiled and headed away to pour her drink, then came back and set the full glass in front of her.

Just then, the bar grew silent as the television showed the mayor standing at a podium.

"Citizens of Covington, it's a privilege to be here with you tonight. It's under horrible circumstances, as these floods have impacted us all, but I am here to assure you that we are going to get through this together. I would now like to introduce Patrick O'Rourke, one of the most powerful, positive, and respected leadership development consultants in the world, who will be working with us to help raise the funds to get Covington back to its former glory. His wife, Lenora, was a beloved part of this community, and as a special gift in honor of her memory, Mr. O'Rourke will be offering his services to us at no charge."

With that, the entire crowd in the meeting hall—thousands of people, as Phillip had been told would be there—stood and cheered.

Juliette leaned forward at the bar as the camera zoomed in on Patrick O'Rourke, now stepping to the microphone. "Ladies and gentlemen, this town is special to me, as it is to you. Though I have traveled the world for many years and have met hundreds of thousands of people in my line of work, I have never found a place whose people are so kind and genuine and hardworking as here in Covington."

Patrick paused as the auditorium filled with thunderous applause.

After a moment, the clapping subsided, and he continued in a strong voice. "I will do everything within my capabilities to bring this town back to what it was—and then to make it better than ever for each of you, as quickly as possible. At this point, it may seem unclear *how* it will happen, but I do know that with faith all things are possible, and ladies and gentlemen . . . I have no shortage of faith!"

Again, the crowd stood and cheered as the camera panned the audience. When the noise died down, the focus returned to Patrick, but the proud, gentle Irishman was suddenly unable to speak, his eyes misty. Thoughts of Lenora and how proud she would be of him, helping her community on this night, came pouring into his mind as he stood motionless.

The auditorium fell silent, as did the bar where Juliette sat watching, and no doubt every tuned-in location in southern Ireland was equally quiet. The man who had dedicated his life to being there for others, stood alone and speechless.

Just then, the camera turned and focused on a man coming from offstage, out of Patrick's view. The crowd saw a handsome, impeccably dressed gentleman walking assuredly toward Patrick O'Rourke.

As Patrick turned and caught a glimpse of the man, he did a double take, realizing the figure emerging from the shadows was none other than . . . Phillip Westford. Patrick's demeanor became one of pure joy as the two men embraced warmly. The crowd had no idea what was happening as Phillip covered the microphone and asked quietly, "Patrick, may I, please?" Patrick O'Rourke, still shaken, gestured his approval, wiped his eyes, and then with every ounce of strength he could muster, excitedly announced, "Ladies and gentlemen,

I would like to introduce a great friend of mine from America, Mr. Phillip Westford!"

As Phillip stepped forward, it was now apparent to the audience who this man in their midst was—the world's most famous lottery winner. The thoughts of what might lie ahead drove the crowd into a frenzy, and they got to their feet and applauded wildly.

At the bar, Juliette sat captivated as she felt a chill run up her spine, realizing the magnitude of the event she was witnessing. All around her, the patrons from the bar had now gathered near the TV, watching the American stand patiently at the podium, smiling and waiting for the clamor to abate.

When the audience in the town hall took their seats once more, Phillip spoke clearly and authentically, as if he was sharing with a group of close friends. "Sometimes in our lives, we are given the divine opportunity to meet a person who can change us forever. That person can help us see through the mist and guide us to what is truly important in these often frustrating and confusing times we live in. Patrick O'Rourke is that person for me."

The crowd was fully engaged as Phillip continued.

"Patrick and his good friends across the globe— José Gonzales in Mexico, David Cairns in the United States, and Ahmet Mansour in Egypt—recently led me to understand that life is not just what we make of it . . . it is what we help *others* make of it. Each lesson

I learned from these men was one that I desperately needed in my own life."

Juliette held her breath, hanging on every word Phillip spoke. . .

"I have always known that helping others is a good thing. But these people showed me that when we unconditionally pour ourselves into the lives of others, the life that gets filled . . . is our own. I can also now unquestionably say if you don't believe in guardian angels, let me tell you, that is *exactly* what Patrick has been for me, and through his generosity and compassion, he has made me see the opportunity I have—we all have—to impact the world every day. It's no exaggeration to say . . . Patrick O'Rourke gave me my life back and helped me rebuild what I thought could never be rebuilt.

"So tonight, I want to pay back that priceless gift by helping each of you get *your* life back—and help each of you rebuild. I am donating $100 million to restore Covington to its former glory as one of the most beautiful towns in all of Ireland. I am happy to let you know . . . this contribution is the entire amount of lottery winnings I have left."

A collective gasp emerged from the spellbound audience.

As her eyes moistened, Juliette put her hand over her mouth in shock. Feelings of overwhelming admiration flooded in as she smiled and softly voiced, "The curse. I don't believe it . . . he's breaking the lottery curse once and for all . . . and transforming tens of thousands of lives at the same time."

Reaching into the breast pocket of his tuxedo, Phillip pulled out a check, then turned and handed it to Patrick and the mayor, who were now standing at Phillip's side. The auditorium filled with deafening cheers and screams, as did the little Irish pub. It seemed as if all of southern Ireland had exploded in spontaneous, unbridled joy. Juliette burst into tears as she looked at Phillip, Patrick, and the mayor, with their hands now joined and their arms raised in celebration amidst the chaos.

Then, despite the excitement, a gruff, heavyset Irish patron next to Juliette turned toward her, shook his head, and shouted cynically, "Can you believe a bloke would give away their entire fortune to a bloody town? Who in their right mind would do that?"

Juliette paused briefly as if to temper her response, then turned toward him and replied firmly, "Only someone who is *truly* in their right mind would do something like that, sir—and there aren't many of those people in the world. Phillip Westford . . . is one of them."

The man glared at her as if Juliette was a lunatic, then shook his head and turned back to the TV in a huff.

At that moment, Juliette was overcome with emotion from the day. Gratitude, compassion, empathy, love—emotions that Phillip had spoken so eloquently of in his story, emotions she had not felt in a year—filled her soul. She wept openly, understanding the once-in-a-lifetime opportunity she had been given to know Phillip Westford—undoubtedly *her* guardian angel when she needed him most.

Her mind was racing. *How could she have been so fortunate to end up in the train car with Phillip? Everything she thought was wrong—the missed flight, the missed train, even the loss of her job at* The Times *and the subsequent "demotion" to Des Moines. It wasn't all wrong, it was all . . .* right.

She managed a faint smile through her tears as she again heard her father's voice remind her, "*Everything unfolds perfectly, Juliette. . .* "

Just then, it occurred to Juliette that Phillip had told her on the train his entire remaining fortune was one hundred and one million dollars, *not* one hundred million as he had just announced to the audience. *Guess he decided to keep a little for himself after all—can't blame him one bit.* She smiled broadly at the thought.

Still caught up in the emotion of it all, Juliette reached into her purse to take out a tissue and wipe the remaining tears from her swollen eyes. It was at that moment she caught sight of a small white envelope with her name on the front. Opening it carefully, she saw a note inside, and what appeared to be a check, which she unfolded with trembling hands. It was endorsed to Juliette McKelvey from Phillip Westford in the amount of . . . *one million dollars.* Shaking her head in disbelief, and trying desperately to dry the now steady stream of tears, she began reading the accompanying note:

To the Host of Juliette Has Found Another Jewel,

I have no doubt Patrick and "the Three Wise Men" will be elated to hear about the brave, talented young woman who is committed to reaching and inspiring a new generation of leaders through the medium of television.

As I said earlier, Juliette, there is no shortage of money—only a shortage of courage and ideas. Now you have a shortage in none of those areas. Use this check to change the world—which you are already on the path toward doing . . .

Until we meet again,

Phillip

Juliette placed the note and check back in the envelope and into her purse, then gently put her face in her shaking hands as she sobbed tears of joy and gratitude. After a few seconds, she slowly lifted her head, wiped her eyes, and then picked up her glass with the remaining bit of wine. Holding the drink up toward the television amidst the continued roar of the pub crowd, Juliette watched Phillip Westford, the man who had changed her life forever, walk calmly off the stage in front of a sea of cheering people. She smiled broadly, took a deep breath, and offered a quiet, heartfelt toast:

"Change the world. That's exactly what I will do, my friend. Thanks to you, that's *exactly* what I will do . . ."

MAY I ASK A FAVOR?

Thank you for reading my book! Would you do me a favor and take a moment to write a short review on Amazon? Reviews are so important to authors like me, and if you would share your thoughts so others can find out about my writing, I would be truly grateful.

If you leave a review, feel free to let me know by dropping me an email at skipjohnsonauthor1@gmail.com so I can thank you personally!

WANT TO GET WEEKLY INSPIRATION FROM ME?

To get new, weekly inspirational stories and articles at no charge—and to stay updated on my release dates for new books—send an email request to me at skipjohnsonauthor1@gmail.com. I'll also send you one of my most popular, free inspirational e-books as a thank-you!

ABOUT SKIP JOHNSON

Skip Johnson is an inspirational author and speaker whose goal is to encourage and empower his audience to live happier, more successful lives.

As a business leader, Skip practices what he preaches on attitude and happiness. In helping to run his family's health club chain in Georgia for thirty-five years, Skip helped steer the clubs to earn numerous national and international awards, including Best Customer Service Club Worldwide out of more than seven hundred locations, awarded by Gold's Gym International in 2000.

Skip received a BA in political science from the University of West Georgia. He is also the author of the inspirational books *The Mystic's Gift* (Book 1 in The Mystic's Gift/ Royce Holloway series), *The Gentleman's Journey* (Book 2 in The Mystic's Gift/Royce Holloway series), The Treasure in Antigua (Book 3 in The Mystic's Gift/ Royce Holloway series), *Grateful for Everything, and Hidden Jewels of Happiness.*

Skip is an accomplished storyteller, known for his motivational and educational talks that focus on exploring leaders' potential to influence culture and increase happiness. In creating his books, Skip draws on a wide variety of life experiences, from teaching college Sunday school in a small Southern Baptist church for many years, to competing on the men's professional tennis tour in places like India and Australia.

He has also earned the designation of Master Tennis Professional, held by less than one percent of sixteen thousand international tennis professionals certified by the United States Professional Tennis Association.

Skip lives outside of Atlanta, Georgia, with his wife, Anne Marie.

Made in the USA
Columbia, SC
18 November 2022

71447504R00093